# COVET LONDON

## A WHO'S WHO AND WHERE TO GO GUIDE

*Carlie Smith Parkinson*

## ABOUT CARLIE

I have always had a passion for business and can still recall the first business I started at the age of five, selling fruit from our garden to a captive market (my Dad's clients). Having personal history as an entrepreneur, it has been a great experience meeting the amazing women in this book. Many I relate to, many I have learned from, and many I have had the pleasure of enjoying their products or services. All inspiring in their own way!

This book focuses on female entrepreneurs because I wanted to show the emotion and dedication women bring to their businesses. It is rarely about the money. Women give their heart and soul to their business - juggling family, other jobs, community, and more, all while pursuing their passion and fulfilling their dreams.

Similarly to many of the women in this book, I couldn't have done it without help. For me, the encouragement came from my loving husband. All entrepreneurs need someone in their corner to cheer them on when days are too long, too hard, or too low, and I'm lucky to have him there. My enabler, he is the one who never lets me quit, and always pushes me to higher heights.

Having the opportunity to write this book has both inspired and humbled me. It has been a privilege meeting amazing women that work hard to offer services and products we need, desire - and covet!

I hope you enjoy learning more about them and reading their stories.

## ABOUT THE GUIDE

To research this book, I first had to re-explore London. I ventured to areas I had never been and found a new appreciation for this amazing city. So many people fall into the trap of getting comfortable within their own local village, and why not? Each little corner of London offers all you need with its own twist, its own pulse and its own specialties. But there are so many more places to fall in love with in this city and I'm grateful that, through writing this book, I've done just that.

The most fun part about going somewhere new is meeting the people that live and work there. London is extremely multi-cultural, and I've learned how the diverse group of entrepreneurs I'd like to introduce you to have contributed to that. For many, the reason behind starting their business was a desire to bring something discovered beyond British shores, something different or delightful, to the streets of London. For others, it was to share their passion, interests and skills - a drive to help and enlighten us.

They are a great resource, whether you are looking for a stylist, planning an event or just want to try something new, these women can help you. They are the women we can rely on to better ourselves and our businesses.

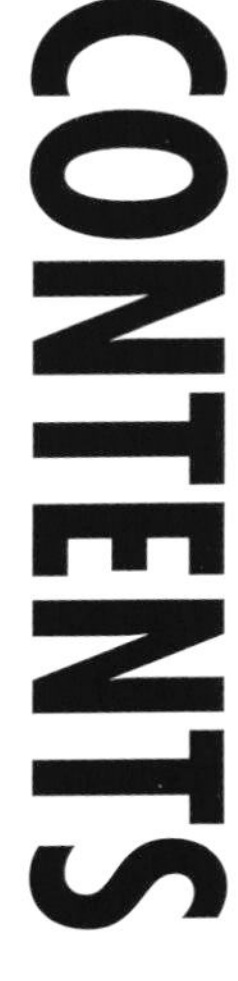
CONTENTS

# CENTRAL LONDON

The heart of London offers everything anyone could need. Busy streets are filled with people rushing to work, enjoying amazing restaurants or taking in a show. The activity is endless and the energy is infectious.

While exploring central London, I discovered shops overflowing with treasures, delectable foods from tiny kitchens, and a clinic filled with health experts offering all you need. Look beyond Oxford Street and you will find an abundance of truly inspiring businesses occupying every available space on every road, all different.

The next few pages are the gems I found in Knightsbridge, Marylebone, Mayfair, Covent Garden, and Clerkenwell.

SMILE
AND THE WORLD
SMILES
WITH YOU
OPEN
A BIT
LOST

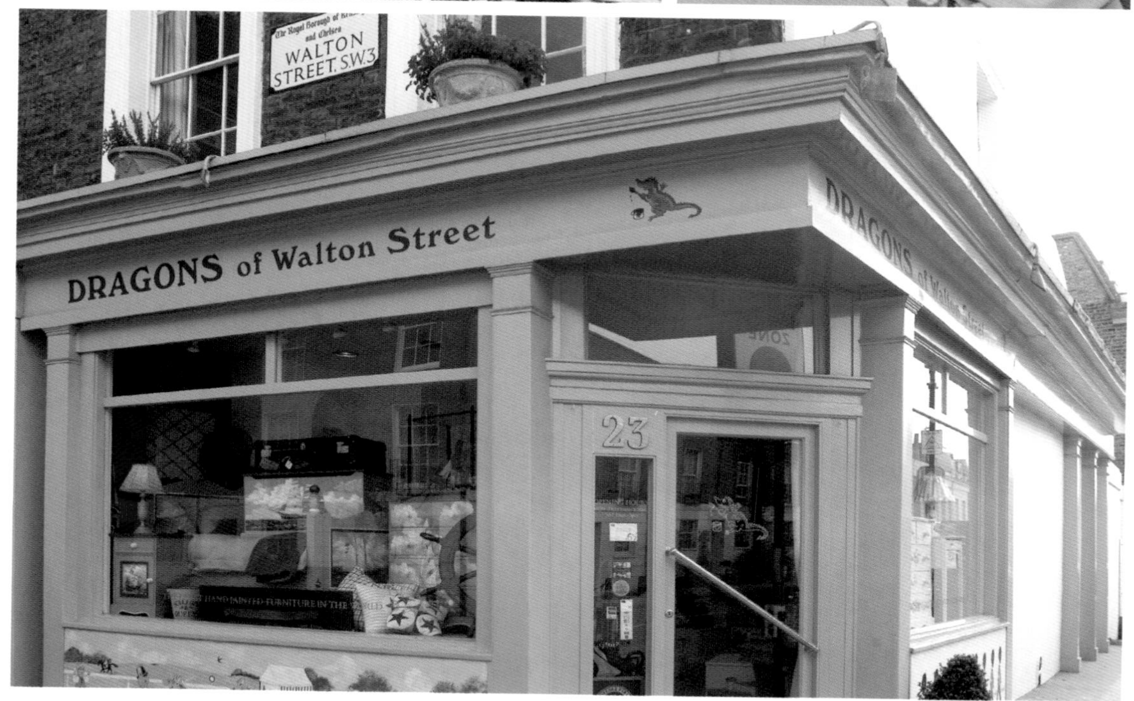
and Chelsea
WALTON
STREET. S.W.3
DRAGONS of Walton Street
23
DRAGONS

photos by Dragons of Walton Street

# DRAGONS OF WALTON STREET

LUCINDA CROFT
23 WALTON ST, SW3 2HX
TEL: 020 3544 2000
ENQUIRIES@DRAGONSOFWALTONSTREET.COM
DRAGONSOFWALTONSTREET.COM

Renowned for the celebrity rooms they have decorated, Dragons of Walton Street sells luxury hand-painted children's furniture. Lucinda Croft inherited the business from her mother Rosie Fisher, who founded it in 1979. Continuing the family tradition, Lucinda and her team of artists add a touch of magic to any child's nursery or bedroom.

Hailing from a family of entrepreneurs, beginning with her grandfather who inspired her mother to open the shop, Lucinda was driven to continue the custom. "It is so exciting creating jobs for people and also creating items that can't be found anywhere else in the world."

The shop is truly one-of-a-kind with an emphasis on bespoke children's furniture. Every piece is hand-painted in their Sussex studio. Artists are available for mural paintings, and some have travelled as far as America to decorate rooms. Customers can choose from a vast range of existing designs or even create their own. The design is then carefully applied to a hand-made piece of furniture.

Although their creations last for generations, many customers have made it their tradition to shop at Dragons. "Now we are dealing with second generation and sometimes third generation families. I once served someone who my mother served 25 years before and was back buying for her granddaughter." Similarly, it is rumoured that Dragons have now designed two generations of Royal nurseries.

# KOHATU + PETROS

JOANNA SALMOND & VARNEY POLYDOR
58 CHILTERN ST, W1U 7QZ
TEL: 020 7486 7737
@KOHATUANDPETROS
INFO@KOHATUANDPETROS.COM
KOHATUANDPETROS.COM

*photos by Annie Armitage*

Kohatu + Petros bring their original, stylish jewellery to Chiltern Street – a part of Marylebone filled with eclectic and independent boutiques. Fashioning necklaces, bracelets, earrings, and pendants from semi-precious stones, sterling silver, and gold vermeil components, Joanna Salmond and Varney Polydor design each piece to be worn and enjoyed every day.

Joanna and Varney take inspiration from the catwalk and translate it into unique and wearable jewellery to delight their loyal customers by complementing the prevailing trends but not being dictated by them. Collections are limited in number, adding to their uniqueness and exclusivity, providing an exciting new experience with every season.

"Each design is created in our Chiltern Street studio. Our customers can even bring in an outfit and we will work with them in our private room to create a centrepiece unique to them!" say Joanna and Varney. "We also showcase the designs of emgerging talents which has proven to be very successul and always inspiring."

Their passion for exotic jewellery is reflected in the name of their boutique, as is their respective heritage. Joanna is from New Zealand and Varney has a Greek background. In Maori, 'Kohatu' means 'Stone' and in Greek, 'Petros' means 'Rock' hence Kohatu + Petros.

Their inventive spirit has also earned them industry awards as well as a raft of loyal, artfully accessorised customers.

KOHATU + PETROS
KOHATU + PETROS

Daisy loves to party!
Invite her to cater for your next party or event!
100% fat free
100% happy
100% healthy
100% delicious
DAISYGREEN
Gourmet Frozen Yogurt
C866 PMV

photos by Daisy Green

# DAISY GREEN OF PORTMAN VILLAGE

PRUE FREEMAN
20 SEYMOUR STREET, W1H 7HX
TEL: 020 7723 3301
@DAISYGREENFOOD
HELLO@DAISYGREENFOOD.COM
DAISYGREENFOOD.COM

Prue Freeman opened her first fixed location cafe, Daisy Green, in the quaint Portman Village. Previously selling her artisan coffee and gourmet frozen yogurt from her mobile fleet on London Streets and at major UK festivals and events (Hyde Park, Royal Ascot, and Secret Garden Party), this Aussie girl wanted to find Daisy a home.

Prue brought everything together and now offers the full 'Daisy' experience. The setting is arty and original. A huge street art collaboration with up and coming street artist Shuby has transformed her once decrepit downstairs into a must see secret garden offering privacy, wi-fi, and lots of inspiration.

Happily serving her specialty items, Prue has also expanded her menu to include a fresh Aussie Brunch, hot smoked salmon (smoked on premises) and an array of healthy interesting salads. She always uses the best quality ingredients, and everything that can be made in-house is, including their famous banana bread, chocolate brownies and fiery chilli red pesto.

The frozen yogurt is handmade in North Wales and delivered fresh to their door.This 100% fat free dessert contains tonnes of probiotics and prebiotics and nothing artificial and with one or more of the enticing flavours available to top this traditional dessert, it can be taken to a whole new level.

"Our toppings challenge the conventional - think balsamic strawberries, lemon curd and homemade meringues, caramelised bacon, avocado soufflé.We resist having a generic topping buffet and offer a smaller, more bespoke range of gourmet and exotic items"

With something original on the always changing menu, Prue's regulars make Daisy Green a second home.The mobile fleet of stand out vintage vans and gorgeous tricycles including Pinky - a 1975 Ford Transit Van - can still be found around town, bringing health and happiness to the streets of London in a high quality, adventurous, and fun way!

# BARNETT LAWSON TRIMMINGS LTD

CAROLINE MARX
16-17 LITTLE PORTLAND ST, W1W 8NE
TEL: 020 7636 8591
BLTRIMMINGS.COM

*photos by Annie Armitage*

Established over 50 years ago, Barnett Lawson, also fondly known as the Aladdin's cave, is a wholesale trimmings shop stocking over 12,000 trims. While being somewhat of a secret destination, in their basement premises just North of Oxford Circus, they are every creative person's first port of call, supplying all kinds of decorative embellishments including ribbons, tassels, braids, fringing, elastics and millinery supplies to film, theatre, and television wardrobes, the fashion industry, designers, visual merchandisers, stylists, and all sectors of the creative industry.

Caroline Marx purchased Barnett Lawson Trimmings in 2001, after selling her PR agency to spend more time with her daughters. Prior to buying it, she took a three-day course that helped her assess what she wanted in life, and gave her the courage, confidence, and clarity of mind to see the opportunity when it arrived.

"I absolutely love this business and have never looked back", she says which, with her creative background and fashion training, comes as no surprise..

The shop is appropriately located in what used to be London's garment district and is easily accessible by public transport making it a great stop on a shopping trip to Oxford Street.

Although Barnett Lawson have an extensive stock, their motto is "If we don't stock it, we can source it", and they pride themselves on tracking down obscure trimmings and articles that their customers have been unable to find elsewhere. They try not to take things too seriously, as the welcoming sign on the door suggests, 'Keep Calm, It's Only Trimmings!'

An institution in the costume, millinery, and fashion world, Barnett Lawson is a hub for established fashion designers, stylists, and design students, and an inspirational destination with a wealth of creative riches for the rest of us!

photos by Keith Morris

# COOKERY SCHOOL

ROSALIND RATHOUSE
15B LITTLE PORTLAND STREET, W1W 8BW
TEL: 020 7631 4590
@COOKERYSCHOOL
INFO@COOKERYSCHOOL.CO.UK
COOKERYSCHOOL.CO.UK

Just steps from Oxford Circus, the Cookery School is a haven where students, from beginner to experienced, can improve their cooking skills and develop a new appreciation for food. Led by Rosalind Rathouse, a cook with over forty years experience, the school uses a straightforward, hands-on approach to make dishes that are simple, modern and imaginative.

Encouraged by her husband, who designed the premises, Rosalind established the Cookery School to combine both her love for teaching and her love for cooking. With a goal to encourage even the most timid cook, she demystifies cookery techniques and removes jargon.

Although she has simplified the process, Rosalind knows the importance of using the best ingredients - "We use organic if possible so that our food always tastes great. We are also very proud of our record in terms of sustainability and ethical ethos. We have been practising this since our inception and long before it was 'cool'."

Rosalind caters to a wide range of students offering corporate training sessions, parties, and absolute beginner classes. She finds many people are in search of really basic cookery techniques and key principles. For more advanced students, classes include pastry, fish and shellfish, sauces, chocolate making and many more. In each class students learn many new skills and an arsenal of new recipes easily incorporated into their everyday repertoire.

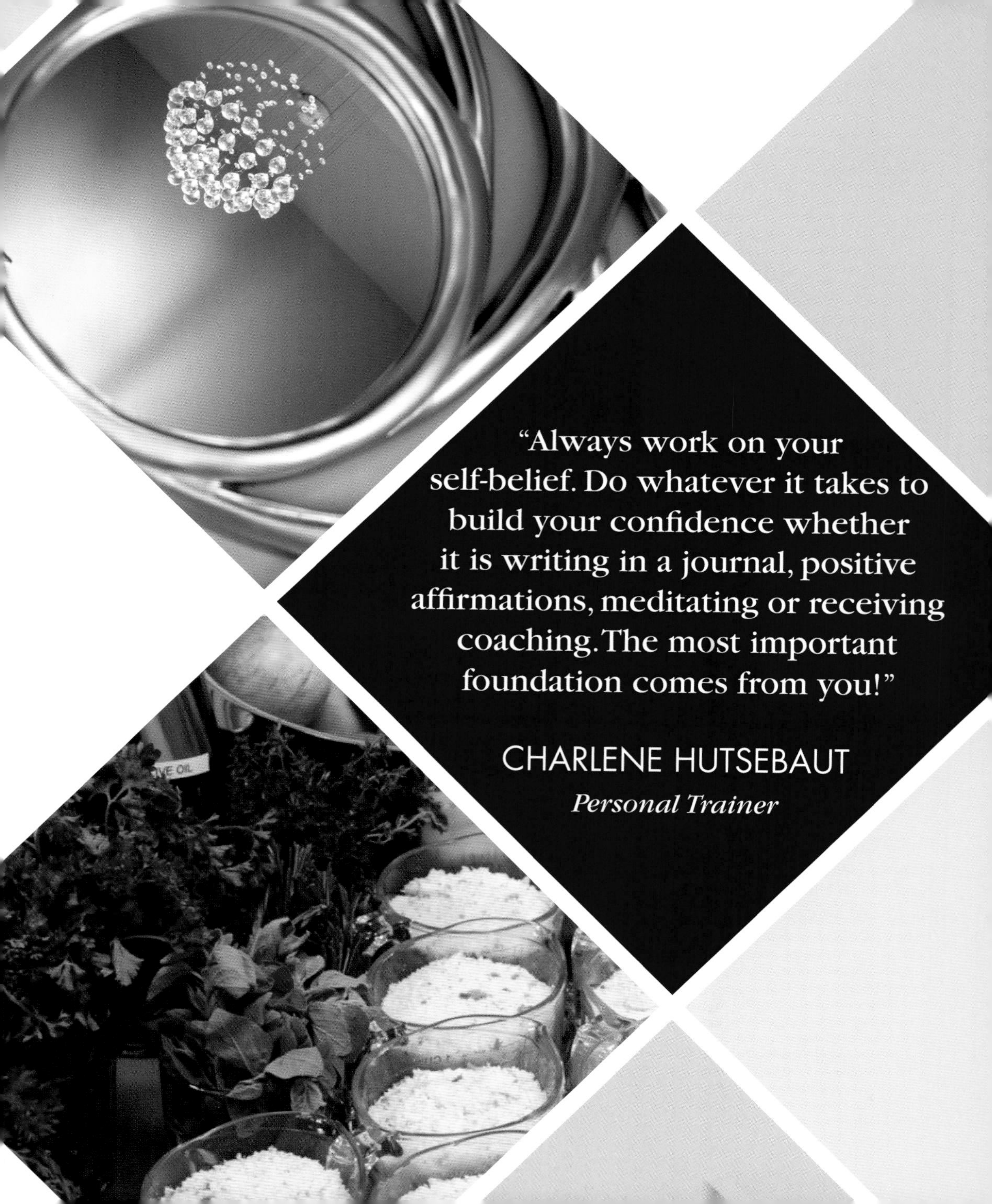
"Always work on your self-belief. Do whatever it takes to build your confidence whether it is writing in a journal, positive affirmations, meditating or receiving coaching. The most important foundation comes from you!"
CHARLENE HUTSEBAUT
Personal Trainer

# 58 SOUTH MOLTON ST WELLBEING BUSINESS CENTRE

MICHAL COHEN-SAGI
58 SOUTH MOLTON ST, W1K 5SL
TEL: 020 7706 1997
@58SOUTHMOLTONST
INFO@KINGYOTHERAPY.COM
58SOUTHMOLTONST.COM

58 South Molton Street helps clients reach their optimum health and vitality, by offering the best treatments and therapies from their team of leading experts, each selected for their superior knowledge and experience in their field. Michal Cohen-Sagi and her husband Noam Sagi created 58 South Molton Street to provide a 360 degree approach to wellness – a relaxing and supportive centre where experts can treat both physical and emotional ailments in a supporting environment where clients are guided to feeling their very best.

Conveniently located off Bond Street, 58 South Molton Street is an "oasis of calm". It allows clients to relax, be inspired and feel supported on their personal journey. Michal and Noam have gone to great lengths to create a comfortable, stylish environment capable of nurturing one's inspiration.

"The atmosphere here is that of a harmonious community based on well-being, professionalism and outstanding service. It's a special place that helps you to become the very best version of yourself, and which I invite you to experience."

Offering her stunning space for private hire, Michal invites businesses to be inspired during their conferences, training sessions or launches. The sophisticated space lends itself perfectly to an exchange of knowledge, team motivation or any occasion to celebrate!

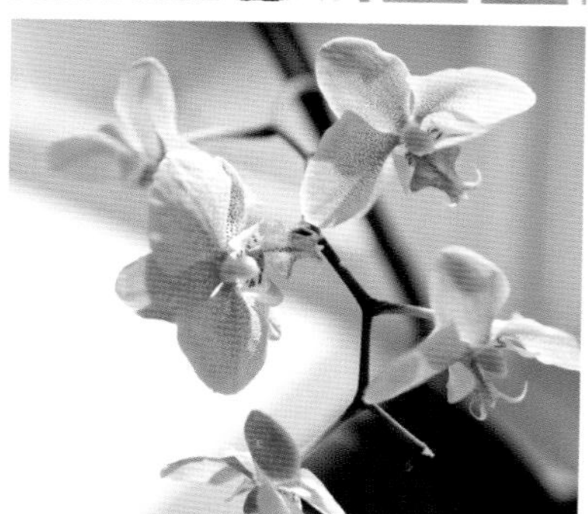

*photos by Annie Armitage*

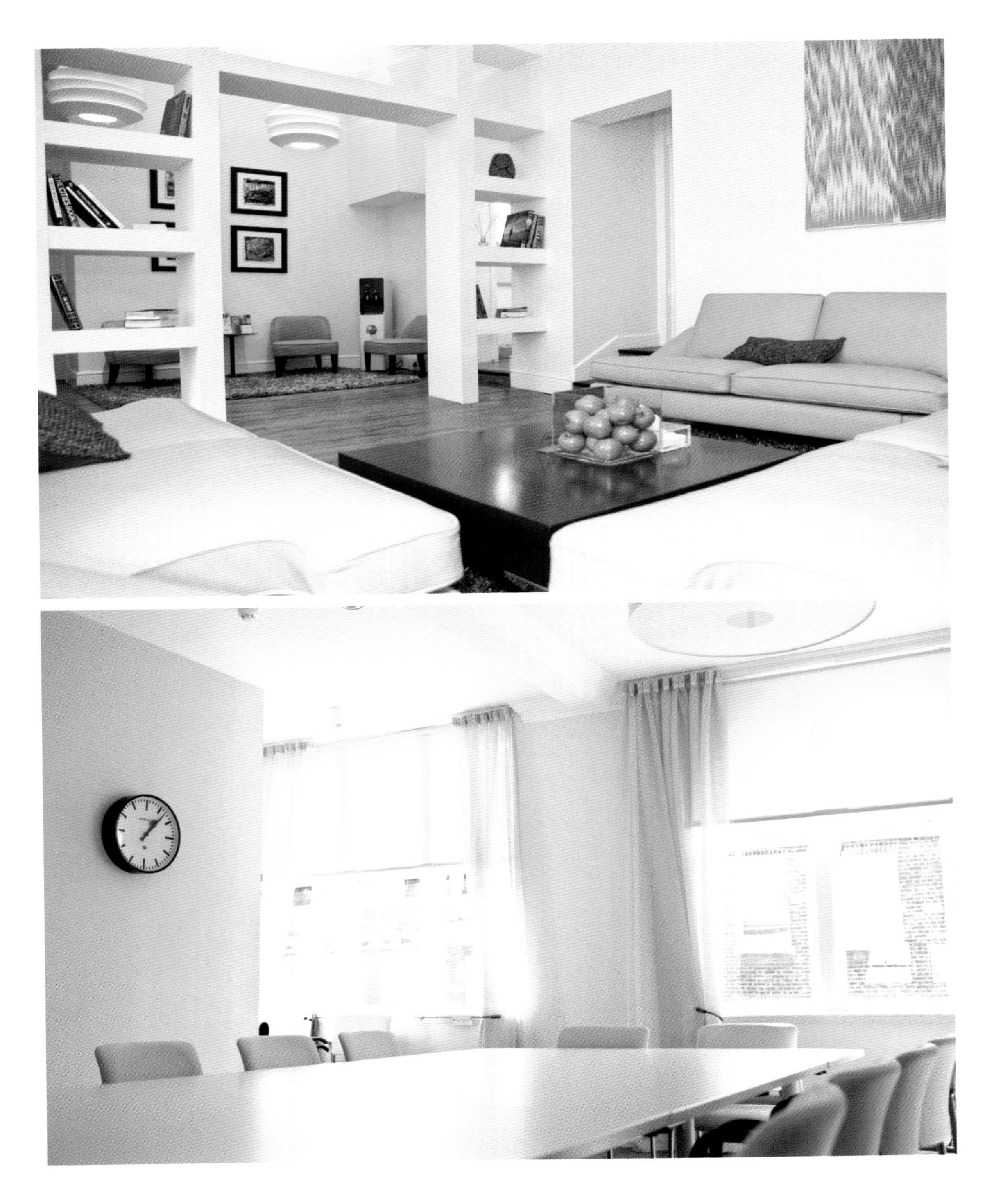
THE CITIES BOOK

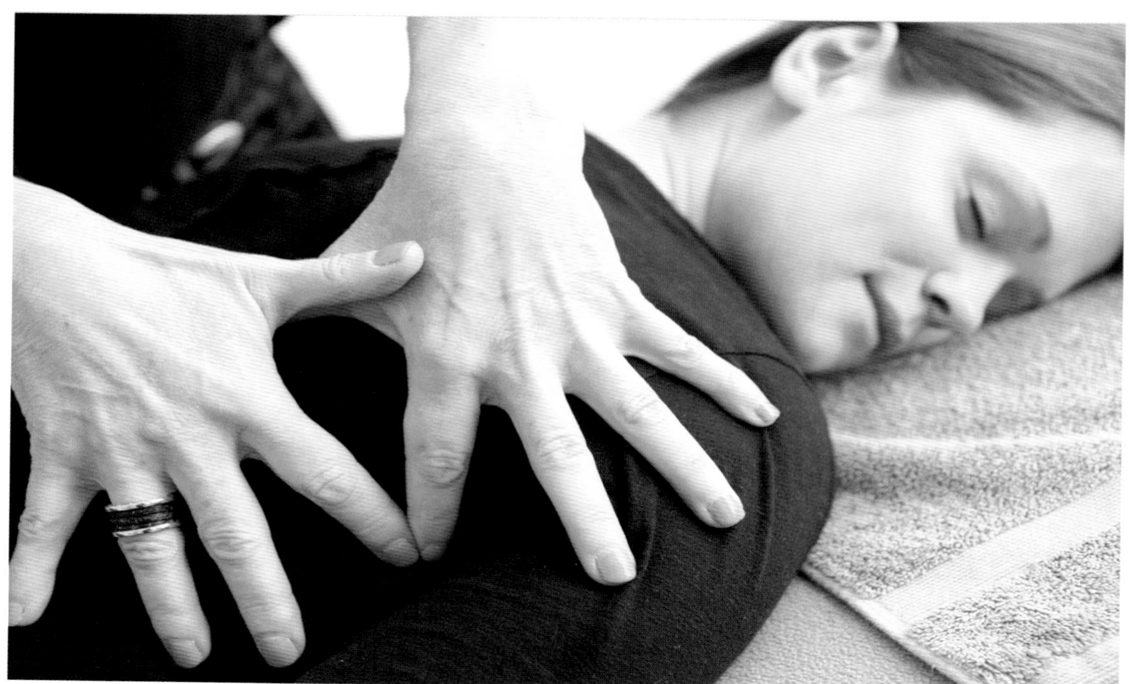

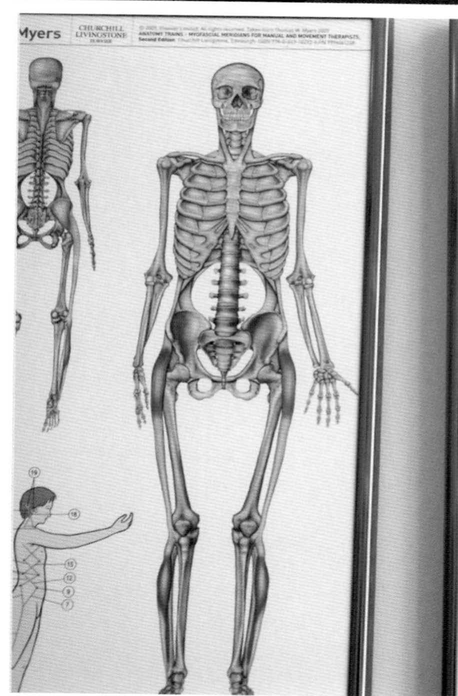
Myers
CHURCHILL
LIVINGSTONE

JUST
BREATHE

*photos by Annie Armitage*

# CAROLINE KREMER

CAROLINE KREMER
58 SOUTH MOLTON ST, W1K 5SL
TEL: 020 7706 1997
@CAROLINEKREMER
CAROLINE@CAROLINEKREMER.COM
CAROLINEKREMER.COM

Caroline Kremer offers personally tailored, powerfully effective treatment strategies to promote balance in the emotional system, aid rapid recovery from muscular pain or injury, improve posture and physical performance, and build greater stability, mobility, and flexibility through the Bowen Technique, Breathing Awareness, and Yoga.

The daughter of one of the UK's early Bowen Technique practitioners, Caroline had first-hand experience with the power of Bowen after a treatment on her chronic back pain.

In 1999, Caroline began her journey to become a Bowen professional and has been practicing since 2004. She uses the Bowen technique to address the whole physical system and offers a means to get healthy and stay healthy long-term. By adding qualifications in yoga and breath work, Caroline has a versatile toolbox to help accelerate recovery and enhance holistic wellbeing.

"I have a deep understanding of the relationship of body alignment, myofascial and fascial stress lines, and the impact of emotional and psychological stress on the physical body."

Caroline uses her holistic techniques to work closely with her clients in maintaining their health, not just fixing it when it goes wrong. "It follows the Far Eastern paradigm of treating a healthy body to maintain a healthy body."

Also in touch with her spiritual side, Caroline looked within when starting her business. "Life inspired me. A desire to be, to grow, and to learn and the realisation that I choose the direction my life goes in with my thoughts, my words, and my actions", an ideal we can all draw inspiration from.

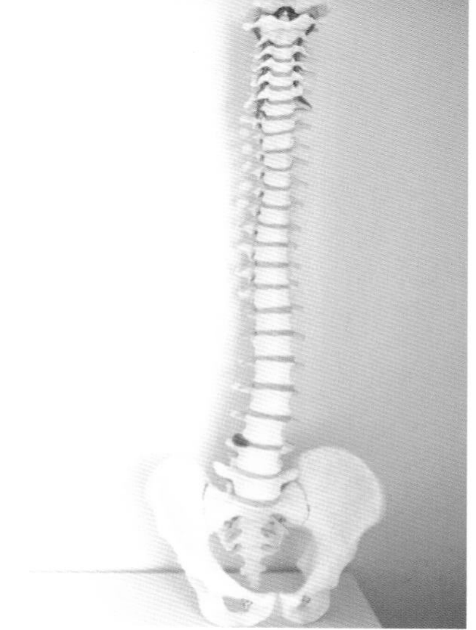

# OSTEOPATHIC CONSULTANCY

AMBERIN FUR
58 SOUTH MOLTON ST, W1K 5SL
TEL: 020 7706 1997
@OSTEOCONSULT
AMBERIN@OSTEOPATHUK.COM
OSTEOPATHUK.COM

*photos by Annie Armitage*

Osteopathy is a form of natural healthcare using a hands-on approach to help restore the body's balance and promote self healing. Amberin Fur, director of Osteopathic Consultancy, treats every age and body type, from new born babies to elite athletes, with her 17 years of experience understanding the workings of the human body.

An important member of the 58 South Molton Street team, Amberin brings her extensive knowledge and a unique service, tailored to provide a bespoke solution, to the patient's care.

Amberin's one-to-one consultations allow patients to experience the treatment and its effects on their pain and their body as a whole. She helps her patients identify their symptoms and what has brought their discomfort, enabling her to lead them on their pathway to health.

"Although my practice is results driven and I am looking to get my patients out of pain, my focus is on the whole patient, often addressing old patterns of trauma, which can be crucial in maintaining a sense of balance and health."

Working with patients who are invested in their health, Amberin takes an active approach and advises on preventative healthcare, improving their health and their lives.

Inspired by her mother, who always fought in the face of adversity, Amberin always strives to fulfil her potential and advises aspiring entrepreneurs to "believe in your skills and follow your instincts. Above all, act - do something positive towards your goals on a daily basis."

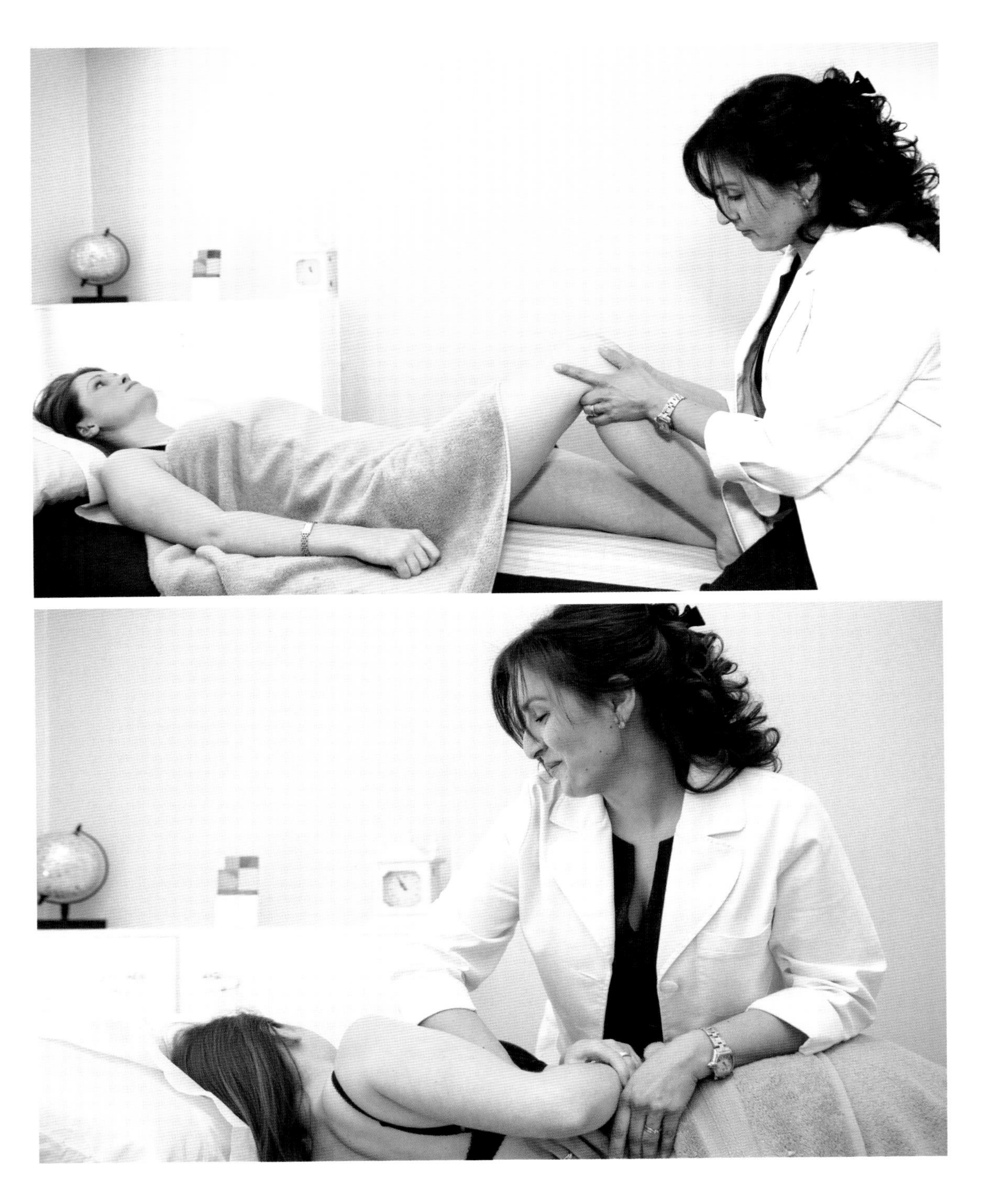

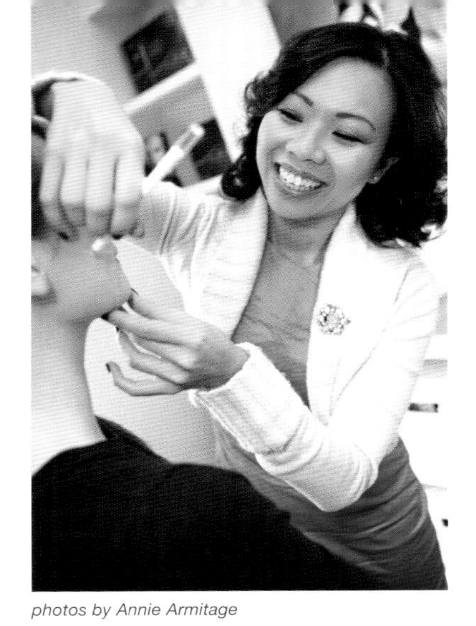

photos by Annie Armitage

# THE SKIN ENERGY CLINIC LTD

DR TERRY LOONG
58 SOUTH MOLTON ST, W1K 5SL
TEL: 020 7706 1997
@DRTERRYLOONG
INFO@DRTERRY.COM
DRTERRY.COM

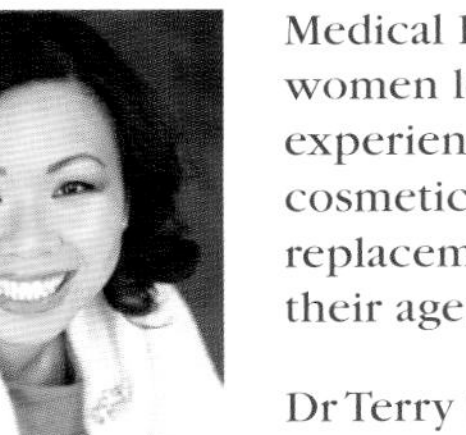

Medical Director of The Skin Energy Clinic in Mayfair, Dr Terry Loong helps women look and feel younger for longer. With over a decade of medical experience, she now specialises in advanced skin treatments, non-surgical cosmetic procedures, and hormonal rebalancing using bio-identical hormone replacement therapy to help her clients look and feel their best, whatever their age.

Dr Terry became "The Skin Energy Doctor" because she believes skin is an extension of our whole being and without energy radiating from within, it will be an empty canvas. She treats skin problems by addressing the internal and external factors that prematurely age us.

After losing her mother at the age of 19, Dr Terry reflected on her relationship with her. "She was the most positive, capable woman you will ever meet. However, her confidence was affected by skin problems such as acne, scars, psoriasis, and eczema." Dr Terry wanted to ensure others didn't share the same plight, and she was inspired to help as many women as she could feel absolutely beautiful and confident in their skin.

Using a unique combination of client education, holistic healing, and fun, Dr Terry takes her clients on a journey through different ages, and gives them tools to better themselves. She begins with skin conditioning treatments - repairing skin health - followed by aesthetic treatments, creating, maintaining and restoring facial harmony, and ending with hormonal rebalancing, creating calm and vitality in the system.

Recognising that women have a tendency to take care of everyone but themselves, Dr Terry believes if women truly take care of themselves they will look and feel on top of the world, creating a ripple effect through their relationships, families, workplace, communities, and beyond. Unsurprisingly, her advice to other entrepreneurs is "to take time out to look after Number One i.e. YOU!"

# BB BAKERY COVENT GARDEN

BRIGITTE BLOCH
6-7 CHANDOS PLACE, WC2N 4HU
TEL: 020 7836 6588
INFO@BBBAKERY.CO.UK
BBBAKERY.CO.UK

photos by Cristina Rossi, portrait by Covet Girl

Owner Brigitte Bloch, also known as BB, brought a touch of Paris to Central London - an escape from the hustle and bustle to the atmosphere of a chic Parisian bakery.

Originally from France, BB moved to London in 2010 and just months later, with help from her husband Phillipe, opened her first BB Bakery on South Bank near London County Hall. She opened her second location on the Queen's Jubilee just two years later, located a short walk from Trafalgar Square and Covent Garden.

When entering either location, the hint of Paris is tastefully peppered through the decor, with original art by BB hung on the walls. BB pays close attention to the details - each item is carefully chosen, including the vintage English china for the tea that is only served by the pot.

The teas are from a Parisian company and have whimsical names, including "Jour de Fete", and enticing flavours with essence of orange, vanilla or rose. They were chosen for their high quality and, not by coincidence, their name, Betjeman and Barton – another BB.

On the menu are both traditional French dishes, including Croque Monsieur, and more English selections, such as the smoked salmon sandwich. Ensuring the fine points are perfect, BB has two teams in the County Hall kitchen where everything is prepared daily. One, a team of Patisserie Chefs recruited from France to prepare all the French delicatessens, and the other a team specializing in English entrees. Even the traditionally English 'Afternoon Tea' has a French twist, with the addition of macarons and the optional glass of champagne.

Ever the entrepreneur, BB is already on the hunt for the ideal location for her third bakery, dedicated to making London a little more French.

**ALSO AT** BB BAKERY COUNTY HALL, 1 BELEVDERE ROAD, SE1 7PB, LONDON

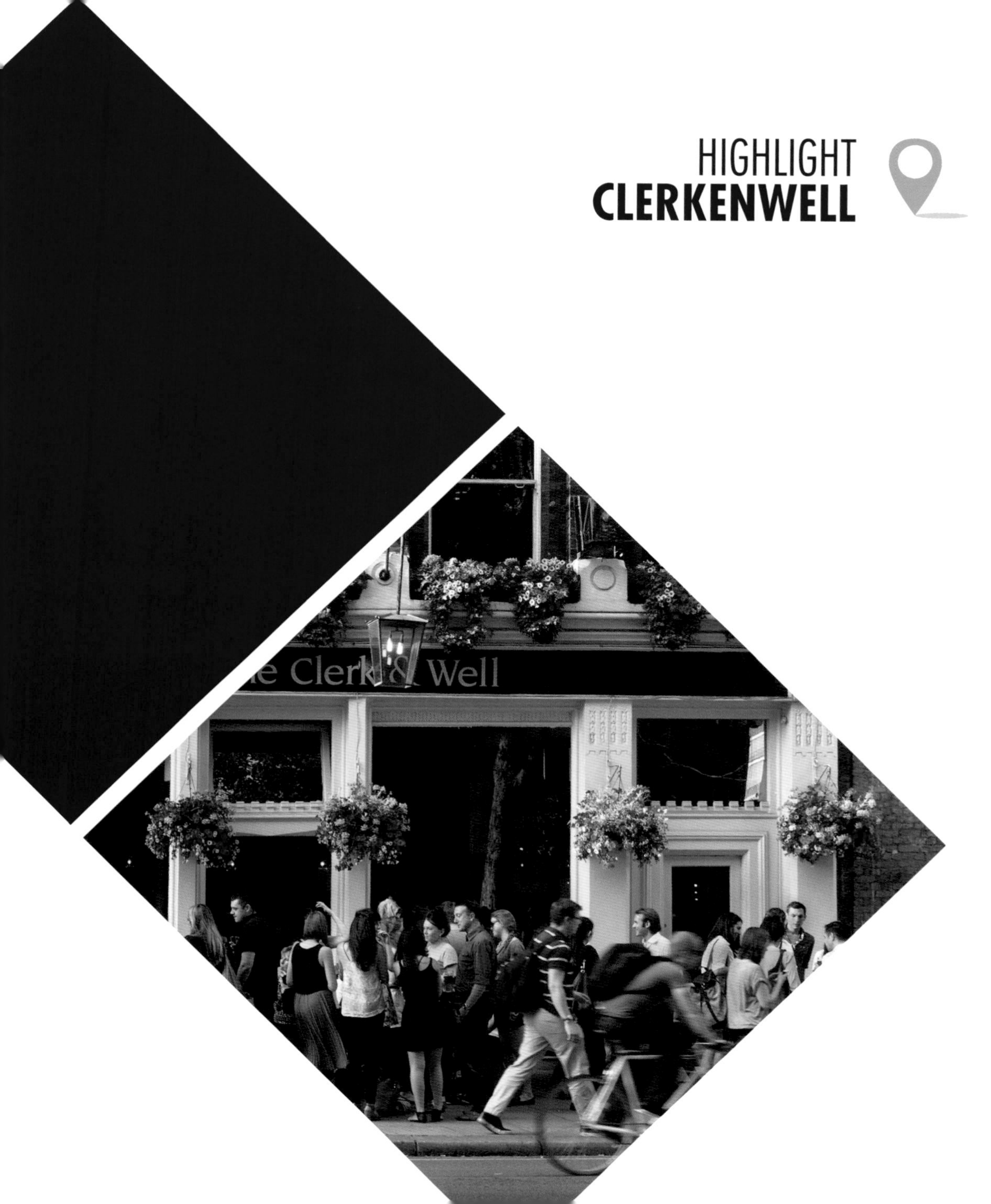
HIGHLIGHT
CLERKENWELL
e Clerk & Well

"Clerkenwell is just on the edge of the City, but has a bustling design-led feel. It is the perfect blend of high-flying City-life, with design and inspiration for a contemporary fashion brand."

POLLY MCMASTER, OWNER OF THE FOLD

"When I came up here I could feel an instant vibe that this was right, and I am so happy I came here as Exmouth Market is so unique."

ANNA FORSLING, OWNER OF THE KLINIK

"Clerkenwell is full of creative businesses and people. Also very foodie and plenty of good places to have the best coffees!"

TAKAKO COPELAND, OWNER OF FAMILY TREE

Clerkenwell has become the design centre of London and is one of the most historic, creative and culturally rich districts in the city. The maze of streets offers new discoveries at every turn with more and more independent businesses flooding to the area.

A hidden gem within Clerkenwell is Exmouth Market. Just off Rosebury Avenue at the Junction with Farringdon Road, this road is bursting with independent businesses, shops, and restaurants. A lively area during lunch for the amazing lunch street market or swarmed after work by City workers and the local creatives coming for a drink.

# THE FOLD

POLLY MCMASTER
84 CLERKENWELL RD, EC1M 5RF
TEL: 020 8965 5600
@THEFOLDLONDON
INFO@THEFOLDLONDON.COM
THEFOLDLONDON.COM

Former City worker, Polly McMaster knows the challenges of finding flattering yet empowering clothing to wear to work.

Recognising a business opportunity and an unexplored niche, she created a chic and contemporary brand, The Fold, to "embrace the professional woman, and make her feel confident and stylish".

photos by Fanni Williams

Polly understands the needs of business women in London. She knows they need a working wardrobe that really inspires them and makes them feel confident. To match their demanding schedules, Polly designs signature dresses and a capsule of separates that can be mixed and matched to create a limitless wardrobe to suit career, social and family activities.

Knowing we all need a personal touch, Polly's clients receive wardrobe advice at her studio located just outside the City in the heart of the design hub, Clerkenwell. Working closely with the women that inspired her to create The Fold, Polly supports her clients in their pursuits.

"We welcome our clients into The Fold. It is our community of high-flying women, where they can feel pampered and understood."

WWW.FAMILYTREESHOP.CO.UK

*photos by Rashmi Gill*

# FAMILY TREE

TAKAKO COPELAND
53 EXMOUTH MARKET, EC1R 4QL
TEL: 020 7278 1084
@FAMILYTREE_SHOP
MAIL@FAMILYTREESHOP.CO.UK
FAMILYTREESHOP.CO.UK

Family tree is a lifestyle shop filled with original, hand-crafted items and oddities by both local and international designer-makers. At home in the bustling Exmouth market, owner Takako Copeland opened the shop in 2004 to showcase the skills of her friends and their families.

An artist herself, Takako is immersed in the creative world. Surrounded by her talented friends from art school, designer-makers met during her time selling at Spitalfields market, and her imaginative customers from the Clerkenwell area, Takako is filled with ideas for, and has wonderful resources to add to, the original items found in Family Tree.

"We enjoy connecting with local makers and small ethical businesses and supporting each other. We choose quality designs with a story behind the business and making/ manufacturing process."

The shop is filled with unique treasures including their own range of jewellery, knit accessories, stationary, and Japanese paper lamps. Exclusive items are also made in collaboration for the shop by local designer-makers. Recognising we live in a world of excess, Takako wants her customers to find items at Family Tree to be cherished - items with a greater meaning and made to last.

# THE KLINIK

ANNA FORSLING
28 EXMOUTH MARKET, EC1R 4QE
TEL: 020 7837 3771
@THEKLINIKSALON
TEAM@THEKLINIK.COM
THEKLINIK.COM

Established in 1998 by Anna Forsling, the klinik is a multidisciplinary, unisex hair salon situated in the creative hub of London's Clerkenwell. This sleek salon has a team of experienced stylists providing everything from cuts to technical colours, ensuring clients leave looking their best.

photos by the klinik

Anna had a vision for her salon. She put extra attention into the design and wanted a very clean clinical look, hence the name 'the klinik', spelt the Swedish way. Wanting her clients to be able to see the process involved in their haircut, Anna installed TV monitors linked to cameras hanging above. "The modern, exciting, new design was created with the idea of showing each client a three-dimensional view of their hair transformation."

Taking special care with her clients, Anna and her team of stylists work to the highest standard in everything that they do. They follow the industry trends and always offer the most advanced treatments. Keeping clients happy between appointments, they offer free consultations and fringe trims.

Encouraging her team to develop meaningful relationships, Anna knows the value of good customer service. "The most importantant bit is that you feel your stylist fully understands what you wish to have and that you feel you have an open communication with them."

# WEST LONDON

Affluent West London offers a wide range of beautiful shops, museums, and cafés. The impressive stores are filled with exquisite fashions - West London society is all about style, even the dogs are dressed to the nines. With many top international fashion brands placing their flagship locations here, it is easy to be overwhelmed, but the real finds are the independent boutiques. Offering everything to adorn you from head to toe, everything to tempt you, and everything to make you an object of desire, you will leave West London feeling, looking, and being better.

In this section, I have included businesses in Kensington, Chelsea, Notting Hill, Kensal Rise, Parsons Green, and Chiswick. I invite you to be inspired by this chic area.

DOLCI FOLLI

# D&ME
# ONE VINTAGE

MARCELLE SYMONS
309 BROMPTON ROAD, SW3 2DY
TEL: 020 7589 2684
@DANDMELONDON
INFO@DANDME.CO.UK
DANDME.CO.UK

photos by Serena Bolton

D&Me is a unique multi-brand boutique founded by Marcelle Symons. It embodies an eclectic lifestyle with a fun and vibrant spirit through its mixture of international contemporary designers and Marcelle's own brand, One Vintage.

Marcelle began her journey into fashion with one-of-a-kind t-shirts that were embellished with vintage trims and buttons. This later evolved into her line, an offering of particular and beautiful reworked vintage pieces sourced from all over the world.

To house her amazing assortment of unique finds, Marcelle opened D&Me, the D standing for her sister Diane who often accompanies Marcelle on her buying trips. Located in South Kensington, D&Me is conveniently situated near the V&A museum - Marcelle and her team are constantly inspired by the vast collection of gorgeous antique textiles and perfectly preserved clothing within.

With a vibrant and varied enough collection to exhibit in a museum, D&Me doesn't just house Marcelle's complete One Vintage line - adding a modern touch to the shop, Marcelle also carefully selects designs from independent designers.

"I've always believed in unique and beautiful pieces rather than labels and trends and I wanted to create a space that would reflect that - a stage for all the emotion and history in these pieces to shine."

With the ever-changing inventory, clients are constantly delighted while exploring the store. Marcelle knows clients keep coming back because "they love that element of surprise, that not only will they find the dress they needed, they will fall in love with a necklace and a bag along the way that completes the look."

SALE

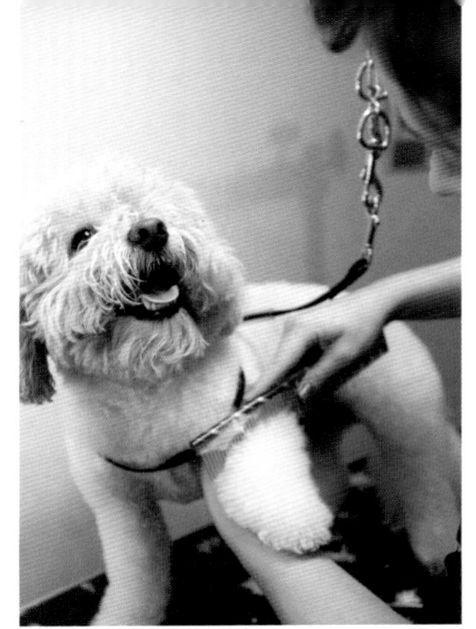

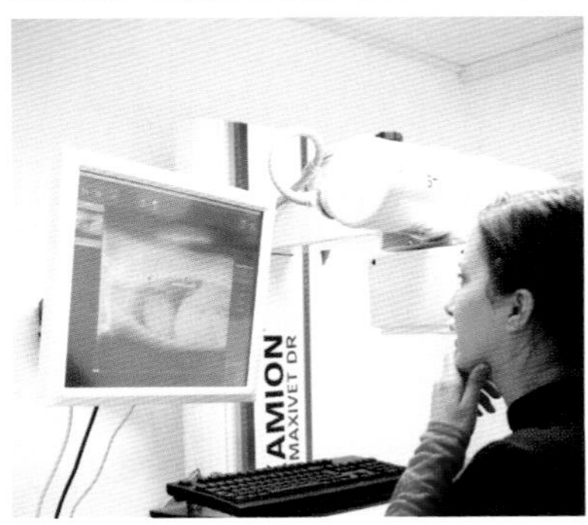


photos by Annie Armitage

# WAGGIN' TAILS LONDON LTD

LUISA HELENA GONZALEZ MIJARES
364-366 FULHAM ROAD, SW10 9UU
SHOP: 020 7823 3111
VET: 020 7352 3324
@WTONLINE
WAGGINTAILSONLINE@GMAIL.COM
WAGGINTAILSONLINE.COM

This once simple grooming parlour has been transformed into a Pet Mecca by serial entrepreneur Luisa Helena Gonzalez Mijares. Now offering expert service and advice at honest and reasonable prices, Waggin' Tails is a one stop shop for your most precious possession: your pet. With a veterinary clinic, grooming parlour, grooming school, and shop, they have everything a pet or pet owner needs or desires.

Luisa purchased Waggin' Tails in December, 2011 with a vision to provide her clients with a place to pamper their pets at a price that allowed them to do it more often. A pet lover herself, Luisa wanted a place to keep animals happy, healthy and safe. "We kept the name Waggin' Tails as a commitment and reminder that the main reason for us to be here is to make the animals happy. Although not all pets wag their tails as a sign of happiness, it is the most well known."

Now with a loyal following of pet lovers in Chelsea and further afield, Waggin' Tails' personal attention has won the hearts of both their clients and their pets.

With a never ending drive to improve the business, Luisa's advice to others involves her perfect day, "Going to bed with a dream and waking up with a purpose...after that, never sleeping again until the dream is reality!"

# HEARTCORE

JESS SCHURING
6 BURNSALL ST, SW3 3ST
TEL: 020 7435 5078
INFO@HEARTCORE.CO.UK
HEARTCORE.CO.UK

Heartcore offers one-of-a-kind, result-oriented Pilates classes. Providing a dynamic and upbeat workout on equipment exclusive to Heartcore, Jess Schuring and her team help their students build lean, strong bodies in four locations across London.

Starting her fitness and wellbeing career in L.A., Jess' results-driven approach and ability to transform people's bodies led to a successful career as a celebrity personal trainer. After moving to London, Jess opened her first Heartcore studio in Kensington offering her very effective, L.A. proven, workout method.

"With Heartcore, I wanted to create studios where people felt welcome and enjoyed being fit and active - turning 'I have to go to the gym' into 'I can't wait to take my next class' by offering energising, challenging, yet fun and result oriented group classes in a positive and beautiful setting."

Now providing numerous workouts at each location, Jess and her team lead hour long full body workouts that are famous for their quick results and addictive nature.

They ensure each client enjoys every moment in the studio, from walking through the door into the relaxing space to leaving with a feeling of accomplishment knowing they have strengthened and energised their bodies, minds and hearts.

*photos by Lucy Williams*

## ALSO AT

KENSINGTON
11A STRATFORD ROAD, W8 6RF

NOTTING HILL
36 UXBRIDGE STREET, W8 7TN

HAMPSTEAD
50 HAMPSTEAD HIGH ST, NW3 1QG

*photos by Loukia Photography*

# RED LEOPARD

MANINA WELDON & KAYE URE
17 CHELSEA PARK GARDENS, SW3 6AF
TEL: 020 7376 4057
@REDLEOPARDSTYLE
REDLEOPARD.CO.UK

Team Red Leopard, led by Manina Weldon and Kaye Ure (Red Leopard Australia) advise on colour, style, make-up, hair, shopping, and provide wardrobe reviews, enabling clients to create their own unique look.

"We transform our client's appearance, which in turn alters the way they feel about themselves."

Thriving in the "villagey atmosphere" of affluent Chelsea, the team of designers are dedicated to helping their customers express their personalities through their personal appearance, and to reach their potential in terms of the way they look and present themselves.

Comprehensive courses can be taken individually or as a package, one-to-one or with friends, all with a light-hearted attitude and lots of fun. Most popular among customers is the colour analysis session because "it makes an immediate impact - people can see for themselves the difference a scarf, t-shirt or lipstick can make".

The team are pleased their customers realise that they are not focused on merely complying with trends or promoting idealised beauty. "Our customers are open-minded and interested in having a wardrobe that really works and goes beyond fashion." This subjective approach is what makes Red Leopard truly special.

"Be authentic
and play to your strengths."
KATE SAWYER
Dandelion

# THE STATE OF GRACE

LUCIA SILVER
53 ST HELEN'S GARDENS, W10 6LN
TEL: 020 7183 2729
@THESTATEOFGRACE
INFO@THESTATEOFGRACE.COM
THESTATEOFGRACE.COM

Lucia Silver created The State of Grace to enable women to dress in clothing that allowed them to express their own style and femininity. They are the only fashion house in London to offer head-to-toe bespoke garment and accessory design, personal styling, and beauty, all located under one roof.

"We offer a red carpet service, previously the privilege of only A-list celebrities. Now it is available to all women wanting to make their own statement for a special occasion, a wardrobe overhaul, or their wedding day."

Supporting women to be natural and authentic in their style, Lucia helps clients who are seeking something truly distinctive for themselves. She designs and manufactures each piece locally and is "entirely focused" on her clients and what is best for them. Although Lucia acknowledges trends in her designs, they are not the focus and are only used if they suit her client.

"There are no collections, but rather a sample room of infinite possibilities, anything is achievable at any time."

The State of Grace made its home in stylish Notting Hill - where local fashionistas bemoan having nothing to wear yet no wardrobe space left in the same breath - the perfect place for a business that is the essence of style and fashion.

*photos by Annie Armitage*

the Jacksons

photos by Rashmi Gill

# THE JACKSONS

JOEY AND LOUISE JACKSON
5 ALL SAINTS ROAD, W11 1HA
TEL: 020 7792 8336
@THEJACKSONSUK
SHOP@THEJACKSONS.CO.UK
THEJACKSONS.CO.UK

Designers of a shoe, boot, and bag label, the Jackson sisters, former fashion PR Joey and costume designer Louise (photo), decided to take it one step further and opened a boutique, The Jacksons, on a quaint road in Notting Hill. It has since become a must go destination for the well-heeled and well-informed.

After starting their careers in fashion by making velvet scarves, the sisters soon felt it was time to move on to something else. With a passion for shoes, they began by designing footwear rich in unique colours with vintage inspired silhouettes - timeless in their beauty.

Their successful home brand is now exported internationally. Taking great care in production, The Jacksons' shoes are made in Spain by family-run factories that draw on generations of craftsmanship, and the leather bags are hand-made by the sisters and their staff in their studio on All Saint's Road.

Their boutique, built on a lifetime passion for dressing up, is the culmination of their efforts. Joey and Louise take great joy in selecting each item and everything found in store is of impeccable quality and taste. The designs are chosen to stand the test of time, not just last a season.

Although believing they fell into the business, the sisters are thankful for the encouragement of their friends and family, and even name their bank manager as one of their most ardent supporters in the beginning.

# PRET A VIVRE

JOANNE CASSABOIS
20 ALL SAINTS ROAD, W11 1HG
TEL: 020 7243 3833
NOTTINGHILL@PRETAVIVRE.COM
SALES@PRETAVIVRE.COM
PRETAVIVRE.COM

Pret a Vivre specialise in made-to-measure curtains and blinds, and fabrics by the metre. Wanting to streamline the buying of custom window dressings, founder Joanne Cassabois opened three London showrooms in four years, complete with fully trained staff advising on colour and style as well as providing instant quotes and free samples, making buying made-to-measure as easy as ready-made.

Inspired by Joanne's time in France, the name Pret a Vivre ('ready to live') says it all - the Pret a Vivre showrooms are designed to help customers picture living with their new window dressings.

"We specialise only in dressing windows of all shapes and sizes so are experts in this field. We know about the fabrics we sell, we show them made up in the showrooms, so it helps the customer visualise and make their decision. Our service is professional but very personal."

This personal service, given to each customer, guides them through the process of choosing from the infinite range of fabrics to suit all styles and budgets, finding the style of window dressing, and measuring and fitting of the curtains and blinds. Offered in-store in London and through in-home consultations nationwide, this service makes a process that can seem overwhelming very easy to live with.

*photos by Lucy Williams*

## ALSO AT

FULHAM
160 WANDSWORTH BRIDGE RD, SW6 2UH
FULHAM@PRETAVIVRE.COM
020 7384 0426

ISLINGTON
69 CROSS STREET, N1 2BB
ISLINGTON@PRETAVIVRE.COM
020 7704 6594

pret a vivre
BRUGES – SILVER BLUE

photos by Annie Armitage

# CERAMICA BLUE

LINDY WIFFEN
10 BLENHEIM CRESCENT, W11 1NN
TEL: 020 7727 0288
@CERAMICABLUE
SHOP@CERAMICABLUE.CO.UK
CERAMICABLUE.CO.UK

Ceramica Blue is a tableware shop with an eclectic selection of characterful and functional dishes, glassware and linens sourced from around the world. Founded by Lindy Wiffen, this specialist shop has a reputation as one of London's best destinations for unusual, beautiful gifts and home-wares. An expert in the industry, Lindy also consults for London's top restaurants, helping them dress their tables. Lindy's influence can be seen in the likes of Ottolenghi and La Petite Maison.

As a child, Lindy grew up eating meals from gorgeous handpainted plates that weren't just saved for special occasions; they were used daily, well loved and appreciated.

"Food and drink are life's essentials, so I love the idea of providing beautiful pieces to eat and drink from."

Offering a wide selection of items, Lindy enables her customers to express their own dining style and find tableware that can truly become part of their home. With a multitude of collections; vibrant or subtle, patterned or plain, Lindy makes it easy to find something to suit each family, something that will stand the test of time and something that will be cherished.

# THE LIBRARY GYM

ZANA MORRIS
206-208 KENSINGTON PARK ROAD, W11 1NR
TEL: 020 7221 7992
BOOK@THELIBRARYGYM.COM
THELIBRARYGYM.COM

Based in Kensington, The Library Gym brings a new approach to fitness. Founded by Zana Morris, this private members training club offers unlimited personal training, tailored nutrition, and outstanding results through their 15 minute training sessions and harmonious classes: chilled yoga, strengthening Pilates, and de-stressing boxing.

"I wanted to create an effective gym that not only offered real results but also, unlike normal warehouse style gyms, was also very intimate and relaxed."

Zana accomplished her goals - The Library Gym has space for you to not only exercise, but also relax and have time to read or simply do some intelligent thinking.

The training sessions have been developed to maximise results. Zana researched the effects of exercise and found that "short intensive training creates a disturbance in muscle tissue, causing it to recruit more fibres and prompting a higher metabolism for several hours afterwards. This in turn accelerates fat burning, improves firm tissue and greatly improves fitness levels. Not to mention that it saves time too!" A fact all her busy clients are especially happy about.

Providing extraordinary results, Zana and her team help their clients lose weight, feel stronger, and look younger.

*photos by The Library Gym*

## ALSO AT

EDUCOGYM
48 HARLEY ST, W1G 9PU
020 7637 5855
HARLEYSTREET@EDUCOGYM.COM
EDUCOGYM.CO.UK

photos by Dolci Follie

# DOLCI FOLLIE

SIMONA WALTERS
28A HEREFORD ROAD, W2 5AJ
TEL: 020 7229 9085
INFO@DOLCIFOLLIE.CO.UK
DOLCIFOLLIE.CO.UK

Dolci Follie is the ultimate lingerie lover's paradise. This decadent boutique offers a wide and wonderful range of luxury and designer lingerie, loungewear, swimwear, and accessories. Each exquisite piece is chosen by owner Simona Walters. Offering a selection of sensational sets ideal for seduction, smoothing shape wear to flatter figures, luxurious loungewear to relax in style, and eye-catching swimwear to dazzle on the beach, there is no shortage of beautiful items to admire and be admired in.

Filled with tempting sweet follies, as the name suggests, Simona fills Dolci Follie with designs from her favourite Italian, French and British brands. She wanted to create the ultimate destination for women searching for the perfect lingerie set.

"Our impressively wide range, from an array of well-known, up and coming, and niche designers, means that every woman will find something to fall in love with when they walk into the boutique."

With daring items, like the cheeky heart-shaped nipple tassels or decadent eye masks, to practical, classical sets, Simona offers it all. She allows her customers to find their comfort zone and then dares them to go beyond it.

Offering that extra level of service, the boutique is a luxurious and opulent space in which customers can relax, take their time, and be seduced by the selection. With trained staff specializing in bra fitting, not only do the pieces look fantastic, they feel fabulous and fit delicately, highlighting all the right curves.

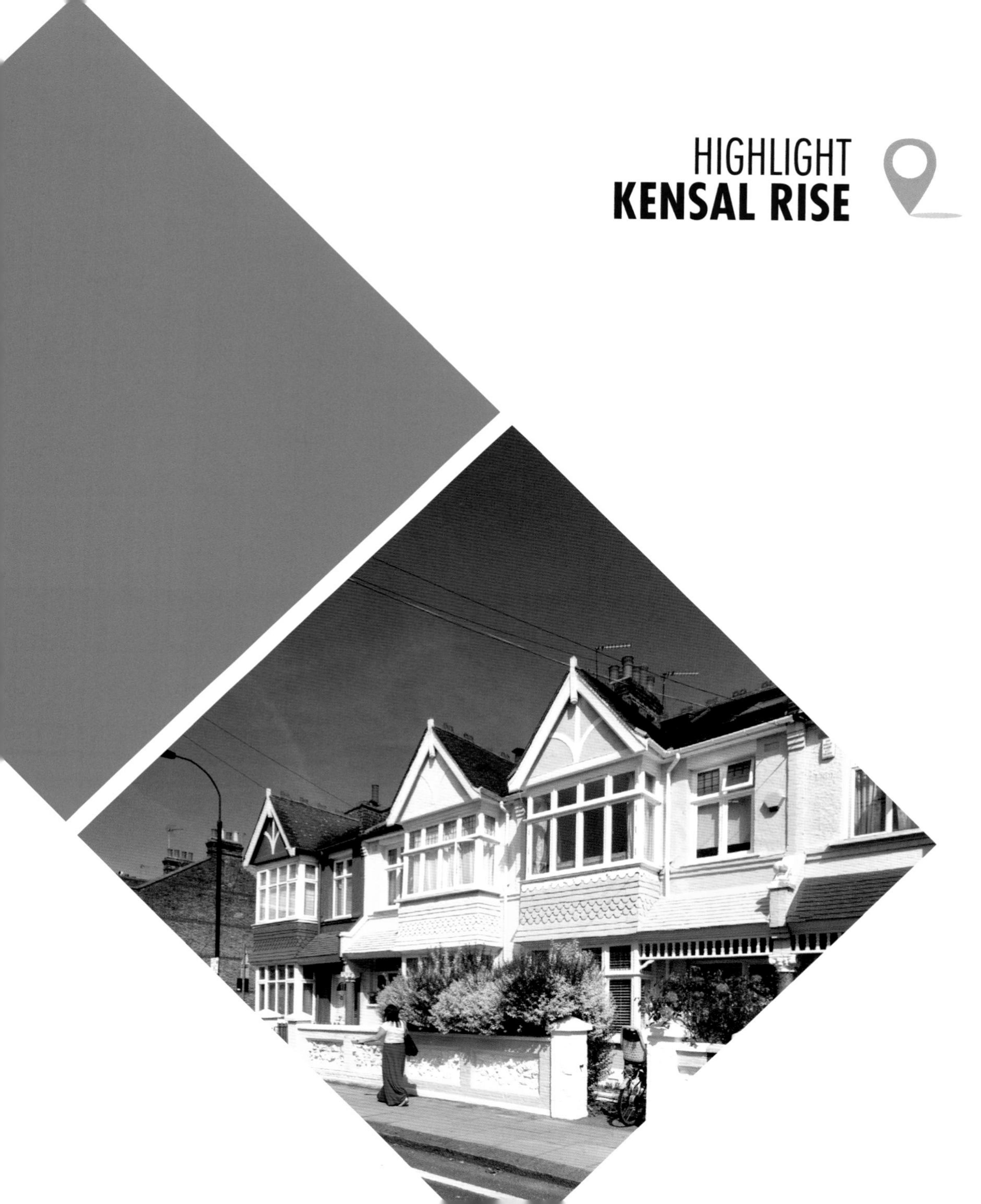
HIGHLIGHT
KENSAL RISE

Kensal Rise was previously a hidden treasure which is now getting the attention it deserves. Home to many celebrity residents, this desirable area has a lot to offer. Drawing influence from Notting Hill, just to the South, Chamberlayne Road has attracted an abundance of independent businesses offering a variety of stylish shops and restaurants and its loyal local customers are eager to support them.

"I love Kensal Rise for so many reasons, one of them being its strong sense of community, and that is hard to find in a big city like London. It is full of inspiring and creative people combined with lots of lovely families from all walks of life. Working and living here makes you feel like you are part of a small village but with all the benefits of a large city. It's perfect."

CORINA PAPADOPOULOU, OWNER OF KIDSEN

"We have a great cultural mix in this part of London, many locals have lived in the area for many years and there is a strong overspill of artists and creatives with Portobello and Notting Hill less than a mile away."

PAULA FITZPATRICK, OWNER OF LOVE KR

# LOVE KR

PAULA FITZPATRICK
98A CHAMBERLAYNE ROAD, NW10 3JN
TEL: 020 8962 5635
@LOVEKRBOUTIQUE
INFO@LOVEKR.CO.UK
LOVEKR.CO.UK

Named to reflect her affection for the area, Paula Fitzpatrick created love kr to bring an eclectic mix of women's fashion, footwear and jewellery to Kensal Rise.

Paula caters to the busy women in her area by filling her shop with interesting brands that are cool and affordable. Her best sellers are footwear, accessories, and separates which are all easily used to update any wardrobe.

Always on the hunt for new labels, Paula spends time visiting fashion shows in the UK and Europe. Her stylish customers rely on her to bring the best of fashion to Kensal Rise.

"My customers are all intelligent women that like to be stylish and not slaves to high fashion and trends, so are very keen to shop at love kr and support new British and European designers."

Paula is also a reliable source for updates when new lines are arriving. "We offer a really personal service, texting customers when we have something new that we think they would love."

Embracing the cultural mix of the community, Paula collaborates with other local businesses and celebrates Kensal Rise and all it has to offer.

*photos by Annie Armitage*

photos by Rashmi Gill

# JIVITA AYURVEDA

ANU PAAVOLA
89 CHAMBERLAYNE ROAD, NW10 3ND
TEL: 020 8964 4993
@JIVITAAYURVEDA
INFO@JIVITAAYURVEDA.COM
JIVITAAYURVEDA.COM

Jivita Ayurveda is an organic centre for wellness in the heart of Kensal Rise offering products and services for ethical and sustainable living.

Created by Anu Paavola, an ayurvedic practitioner, this welcoming space offers relaxing organic treatments, healing products and a wide range of organic foods.

Anu provides all things ayurvedic and draws on the rich Indian heritage of the traditional system of medicine.The name 'Jivita Ayurveda' originates from ancient Sanskrit and means 'knowledge and vitality for life', an ideal that embodies Anu's vision for the centre.

Encouraged by her loyal customers, Anu sought out a space to expand her business beyond one-on-one consultations."I was given plenty of positive feedback for my work and that encouraged me to push my business a bit further and create not only a treatment space but also a retail area under the umbrella of organic health."

Now at home within the health conscious and ethically motivated community of Kensal Kise, Anu has become a valuable member, bringing with her the healing powers of Ayurveda.

photos by Rashmi Gill

# KIDSEN

CORINA PAPADOPOULOU
111 CHAMBERLAYNE ROAD, NW10 3NS
TEL: 020 8969 7565
@KIDSEN
ENQUIRIES@KIDSEN.CO.UK
KIDSEN.CO.UK

Corina Papadopoulou created Kidsen in the heart of Kensal Rise. Kidsen is a fun, friendly, and award winning children's store stocking Scandinavian inspired products ranging from classic wooden toys and Swedish nursery furniture to beautiful and practical children's clothes from some of Scandinavia's best brands.

After retiring from a career as a Producer with MTV to have children, Corina saw a business opportunity in the up-and-coming Kensal Rise area for a unique children's shop. "With no retail experience whatsoever, but with tonnes of belief, enthusiasm, and stamina I decided to start Kidsen. I knew where I wanted the shop, and once I got my premises the rest kind of fell into place."

The shop name came as a light-bulb moment while Corina was reading a Swedish parenting magazine. "The Swedes have taken the word 'kid'and 'Swedified' it by calling their own children 'Kidsen'. It was a perfect name for a kid's shop stocking Scandi goodies in the UK!"

Five years later, Kidsen has won numerous awards and is happily serving the loyal locals of Kensal Rise along with shoppers who have journeyed across London for the unique goods and quality clothing. Also known for their expertise in children's footwear, customers both little and big feel 'at home' in their store.

"Customers often prefer us to department stores or web stores because they know they will get that extra service which only a small independent store can supply."

LUCKYBOYSUNDAY

SCOTTISH FINE SOAPS
Au Lait
Body Milk
Bathing Milk
SINCE 1974
THE
SCOTTISH FINE SOAPS
COMPANY
Au Lait
Moisturising
Milk Soap
Savon au Lait
NET WT.100GM • 3.5OZ

ESTELLA BARTLETT
ESTELLA BARTLETT
GANDYS

*photos by Serena Bolton*

# INDIAN SUMMER

RUTH GREEN
624C FULHAM ROAD, SW6 5RS
TEL: 020 7731 8234
RUTH@INDIANSUMMERSHOP.COM
INDIANSUMMERSHOP.COM

Indian Summer is a treasure trove of shabby chic girliness. Owner Ruth Green fills her shop with unique and one-of-a-kind gifts and goodies - items you didn't imagine needing before, but now can't live without.

At just 20 years old, Ruth went from "Saturday girl" to shop owner. She always loved the idea of owning her own store and got plenty of practice as a child, emptying her mother's cupboards and selling jelly and pasta to her imaginary customers. She has now replaced the jelly and pasta with beautiful items carefully chosen at antique markets or sourced from small designers and has real customers whose loyalty has seen her through the last 9 years.

"I wanted to create a shop that offered a complete shopping experience. Somewhere that sold all the things that I loved but also offered customers something personal where they could come have a chat while we helped them find the perfect present."

Ruth has remained true to her dream as, over the years, she has made friends with many of the locals in the Parsons Green community. She ensures her customers enjoy their time at the shop and even provides entertainment, with a section full of retro toys to keep little people (and their dads) happy!

# GROVE PARK DELI

JANICE TIMOTHY
22 FAUCONBERG ROAD, W4 3JY
TEL: 020 8995 8219
@GROVEPARKDELI
INFO@GROVEPARKDELI.COM
GROVEPARKDELI.COM

Grove Park Deli's owner, Janice Timothy, feeds the Chiswick community excellent home cooking every day, including breakfast, lunch and main courses to take away. With a warm and friendly welcome and additive free, affordable food, why would anyone eat at home?

After a culinary career that took Janice from Hong Kong to Dublin and everywhere in between, she decided to take the leap and start her own business. In June 2003, Janice became her own boss and the proud owner of the Grove Park Deli, sharing her culinary delights and zeal for food with the Chiswick community.

"They really love the deli. They always give me feedback and are very encouraging - they say our sausage rolls, with their French butter puff pastry, home-made onion jam and Dijon mustard, are addictive!"

Using her broad chef skills, Janice leads her team in cooking to gourmet standards using the finest ingredients and proving that fine quality can be affordable. The menu offers deli favourites with a twist - unusual salads, including Broccoli, Bacon and Cashew and Spicy Mango Crunchy.

Janice now also feeds the masses her home cooked delights at private events through her catering services, keeping her encouraging and loyal customers happy!

photos by Annie Armitage

## ALSO AT

RICHMOND
THE ALBERTS DELI
2 WORPLE WAY, TW10 6DF
020 8617 3029
INFO@THEALBERTSDELI.COM
THEALBERTSDELI.COM

# NORTH LONDON

North London offers a vast variety within the villages it is comprised of. Hampstead's leafy heath couldn't be more different from Islington's urban influence, yet every part of North London is special and treasures can be found at every turn. While walking through Islington I wandered into Cross Street - an oasis of chic boutiques - and by taking a turn into an alley in Hampstead, I discovered Mystical Fairies and all its magic.

In this section, I profiled businesses in Hampstead, Islington, Highgate, Crouch End and Stoke Newington, but there are many more amazing villages to be discovered.

# BLUE DAISY

PAULA OPPENHEIMER
13 SOUTH END ROAD, NW3 2PT
TEL: 020 7681 4144
@BLUEDAISYSTORES
INFO@BLUE-DAISY.COM
BLUE-DAISY.COM

photos by Lucy Williams

A unique boutique for babies and toddlers, Blue Daisy only stocks the very best products from around the world. Choosing each item carefully, owner Paula Oppenheimer uses her strong focus on design, quality and excellent value for money to ensure only the best buys are offered in store. She selects toiletries with nurturing ingredients, clothes with original designs, equipment with top functionality, and toys with irresistible playfulness, each meeting her own high standards.

After Paula had her first child she made a number of expensive mistakes, purchasing items which seemed indispensable at the time but in reality only gathered dust. This, combined with the frustration of not easily being able to find the items she did need (like wellies in Summer), made her realise she couldn't be the only one experiencing these challenges.

Encouraged and supported by her husband, Paula's goal was to make all those unexpected essentials available under one roof and supply a product selection that customers could trust, making life as a parent just a little bit easier.

Suitably named after a flower whose genus, Felicia, means happiness, the name Blue Daisy represents all Paula strives for. "For the most part our customers are in a tremendous and transformative period of their lives, and we get to share that wonder and excitement with them."

Blue Daisy provides all the parenting essentials, and is a great place to find a gift for a new parent, conveniently located just a few steps from the Royal Free Hospital.

popet

# SUZANNE FERREIRA PHYSIOTHERAPY

SUZANNE FERREIRA
96 C SOUTH HILL PARK, NW3 2SN
TEL: 020 7209 4912
@SUZFERREIRAPHYS
INFO@SUZANNEFERREIRAPHYSIO.COM
SUZANNEFERREIRAPHYSIO.COM

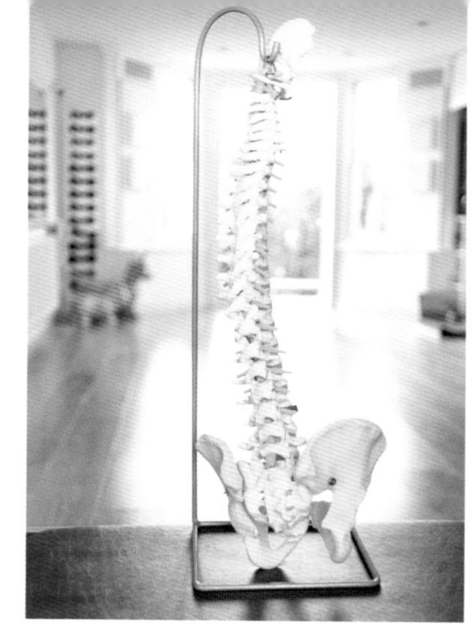

photos by Beatrix Fuhrmann

Suzanne Ferreira Physiotherapy is a boutique studio overlooking beautiful Hampstead Heath. The tranquil environment embraces a spa-atmosphere where clients receive Physiotherapy, Pilates, Yoga, Osteopathy and Massage from Suzanne and her team of inspirational, knowledgeable Instructors.

After a career of working in various sterile and soulless studios followed by a 4-month sabbatical in Italy, Suzanne decided to build a studio of her own, one in which clients are surrounded by beauty and feel at ease, a place where her team can help people restore, optimise and harmonise themselves.

Through individual Physiotherapy and small Pilates and Yoga sessions, Suzanne and her team build deep bonds with their clients and are motivated by the relief, hope and enthusiasm their help brings on a daily basis. They have trust-based relationships with their loyal clientele, who appreciate their honesty and transparency.

"There is not one day that I do not feel emotional when I see the smile of success and achievement on the face of one my clients. There is also not one day where I don't feel emotional when I see the desperation in people with pain and discomfort. Helping people is the only inspiration I need."

Living her life with passion and helping people, Suzanne has found her place in the beautiful Hampstead scenery. She encourages others to "listen to those dreams inside...once you find it... *go for it*".

# MYSTICAL FAIRIES

VERONICA FORD
12 FLASK WALK, NW3 1HE
TEL: 020 7431 1888
INFO@MYSTICALFAIRIES.CO.UK
MYSTICALFAIRIES.CO.UK

A place where dreams come true, Mystical Fairies is a shop filled with all the things little girls' love. Overflowing with pink and sparkles, Veronica Ford's shop displays a vast array of fairy and princess goods. With fairies behind the counter, a visit to Mystical Fairies is like walking into wonderland.

*photos: portrait and this page top by Annie Armitage; this page bottom and next page by Mystical Fairies*

After becoming a mum, Veronica realised how much she loved organising children's parties and all things pink and sparkly. Inspired by her daughter Abbi, who is still her little princess; she combined her loves and created a unique shop. "That was almost 12 years ago, and I still love it now."

Adored by both mums and their little princesses, customers plan visits to Mystical Fairies to say hello and stock up on fairy goods. During school holidays they can also spend the morning at Fairy School or Princess Academy where little girls craft themed arts, decorate fairy cupcakes, get makeovers, or just join in the dancing, disco and games.

For special events, the princesses and fairies are available for parties at the shop in the fabulous fairytale venue or will even come to visit and turn a birthday party into an entertaining extravaganza. Their motto is "No tantrums, just tiara's!" and with creative, energetic and generous performers every child is left enchanted.

# TALLULAH

NICOLA ADAMS
65 CROSS ST, N1 2BB
TEL: 020 7704 0066
@TALLULAH_LONDON
NICOLA@TALLULAH-LINGERIE.CO.UK
TALLULAH-LINGERIE.CO.UK

Tallulah, a lingerie boutique, help the women of Islington find great fitting undergarments. Filled with independent lingerie designers and classic French labels, owner Nicola Adams provides an eclectic mix of items with something for all shapes, tastes and budgets.

With a personal pet peeve for poorly fitting lingerie and recognising a gap in the Islington market, Nicola set-up shop just 8 months after her first child, a boy, was born. She had always loved the name Tallulah (from the film Bugsy Malone) and, unable to use it for her son, it was her first and only choice for her second baby - her new store.

Tallulah is now a favourite for many and a nominee for a number of consumer awards. Nicola prides herself on the customer service she and her team provide. "We give women a va-va-voom experience. We love helping hesitant visitors buy pieces they might not have bought, but that boost their confidence and give them a spring in their step."

Nicola dresses her loyal customers through first dates, engagements, weddings, pregnancies, breast feeding and beyond, always ensuring they are confident in what they have on underneath.

"I love the sassiness a great set of lingerie gives you - it lifts your mood, changes your walk...it's your little secret!"

*photos by Tallulah*

# WILD SWANS

CAROLINE VAN LUTHJE
54 CROSS STREET, N1 2BA
TEL: 020 7354 8681
@WILD_SWANS
INFO@WILD-SWANS.COM
WILD-SWANS.COM

Bringing a little Scandinavian style to the villagey parts of Islington and Chiswick, Wild Swans has built a reputation for its individual clothing and one-of-a-kind service. Stocking lines from Denmark, Norway and Sweden, owner Caroline Van Luthje brings originality to the independent market.

"Before I opened Wild Swans, I bought most of my clothes on trips back home to Denmark. I felt that even the London independent market was very similar, and everyone was stocking the same labels."

Determined to differentiate herself and emulate her inspiration, long-time friend and Danish fashion designer Ann Wiberg, Caroline fills her store with unique and often up-and-coming fashion brands including many exclusive to Wild Swans.

Going above and beyond for her customers, Caroline and her team strive to provide the best service possible. "We go a long way to help and assist our customers. And we always feel we can do better, so we constantly try to be better buyers, give better service, listen to feedback and improve."

Wild Swans shops are filled with unique designers and customers, all as beautiful and gracious as the birds the store is named after.

*photos by Beatrix Fuhrmann*

## ALSO AT

CHISWICK
14 DEVONSHIRE ROAD, W4 2HD
020 8742 8555

# RAY STITCH

RACHEL HART
99 ESSEX ROAD, N1 2SJ
TEL: 020 7704 1060
@RAY_STITCH
INFO@RAYSTITCH.CO.UK
RAYSTITCH.CO.UK

With a goal to bring haberdasheries back to the High Street, Rachel Hart created Ray Stitch, a stylish shop selling beautiful fabrics, trims and sewing accessories. More than just a store, Rachel has incorporated a coffee/sandwich bar on the ground floor and space for sewing classes and events in the basement below.

An avid maker of all things, Rachel desired a shop where she could find good quality materials and all the necessary tools and accessories for sewing and crafting in one place. Inspired and encouraged by her friend and textile designer, Emma Sewell, she made the leap and created her modern haberdashery shop.

Rachel's inviting space offers everything. Customers are often seen crafting in the shop window or busy learning how to make their own clothes in the popular classes downstairs. Remaining committed to a conscientious approach, Rachel considers the environmental impact and fair trade practices of production when choosing the products found in the store. Many of them are organically or sustainably produced.

The shop is suitably named after Rachel, also known as Ray. Coincidently, a 'ray stitch' also exists. It is a type of stitch where the stitches radiate from the centre like the rays of the sun; similarly Ray Stitch brings a little sunshine to the crafters in Islington.

*photos by Ray Stitch*

JANOME

"Believe in your projects, and always share your ideas with others and listen to their advice! If you have determination you will succeed. It's better to feel remorse than to have regrets."

HELENE ALLEN

*Little Paris*

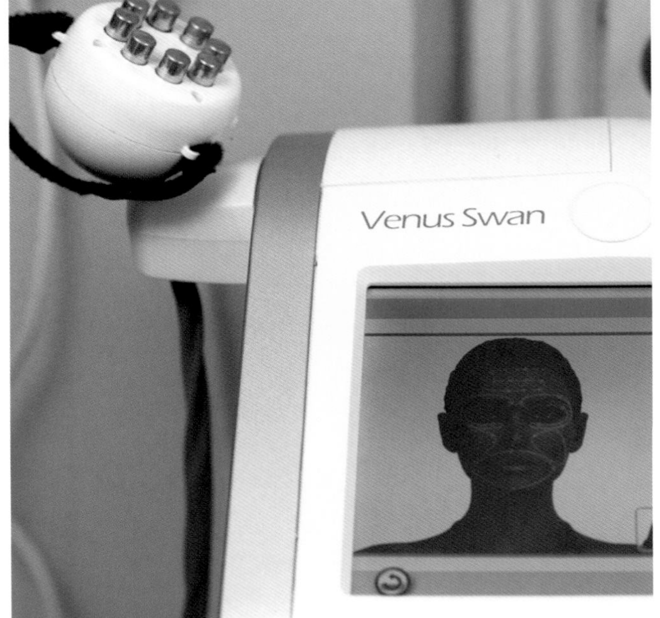
Venus Swan

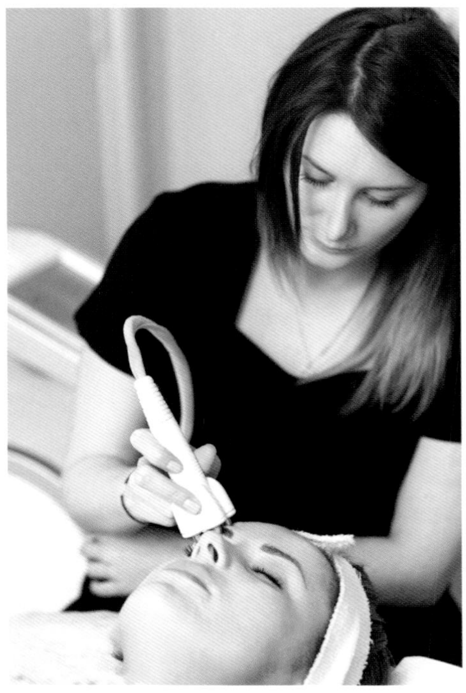

photos by Beatrix Fuhrmann

# FACE IT

DONNA GLAZER
17 HIGHGATE HIGH ST, N6 5JT
TEL: 020 8340 1770
@FACEIT_CLINIC
INFO@FACEIT.UK.COM
FACEIT.UK.COM

At the top of the hill in Highgate sits a hidden treasure for anyone with skin problems. Face It, as the name implies, are experts in facial skin. Donna Glazer and her team attend the latest skin symposiums, study and train in the physiology of the skin and the science of cosmetic chemistry to ensure the clinic offers the latest service with the most advanced technology in skin treatments.

"We love our work and love to help our clients." says Donna, and they appreciate it. The positive word of mouth brings them from far and wide, returning to Face It for the expert help and friendly advice.

Fascinated by the skin and determined to succeed, Donna never rested on her laurels, and after 25 years she still has the same passion, drive and great skin as when she first started.

"We are constantly looking for ways to improve and learn more so we can always offer our clients the treatments and products that not only claim to work, but that we know work from our own experience."

In addition to being experts in skincare, Donna and her therapists offer IPL hair removal and body treatments, taking care of the skin all over your body, not just on your face.

# LITTLE PARIS

HELENE ALLEN
39 PARK ROAD , N8 8TE
TEL: 020 8340 9008
@LITTLEPARISSHOP
HELENE.ALLEN@LITTLEPARIS.CO.UK
LITTLEPARIS.CO.UK

With an enthusiasm for Parisian decor and a desire to share her discoveries, Helene Allen fulfilled her passion in 2009 by creating a home for her collection of antiques and beautiful French pieces. Little Paris boutiques, in Crouch End and Islington, offer an eclectic range of authentic and vintage furniture, curiosities and accessories sourced regularly from the full-size, equally eclectic French capital.

"A little piece of Rive Gauche in London - I wanted to bring elements of everything I adore from France to my new home, England. To create a space which is inviting, unique and homely, and which would embody the spirit of the France I know and love."

Transporting Paris to London one piece at a time, Helene brings new items from France every three weeks. In addition to the antiques and furniture, Little Paris houses contemporary French designed jewellery, Parisian scarves and hats, and a home brand of leather bags.

Helene's passion for French items has both attracted and spread to her loyal following. She relates to her customer's needs so well that she can easily identify pieces that will fit perfectly in their home, bringing a little touch of Paris to each little piece of England.

*photos by Beatrix Fuhrmann*

## ALSO AT

ISLINGTON
262 UPPER STREET, N1 2UQ
020 7704 9970

CONTINUES I ET II
WOODEN DISPLAY CABINET £650

SOURCE PIERVAL

*photos by Lucy Williams*

# ROUGE

LEI YANG
158 STOKE NEWINGTON HIGH ST, N16 7JL
TEL: 020 7275 0887
LEI@ROUGE-SHOP.CO.UK
ROUGE-SHOP.CO.UK

Lei Yang brought a bit of China to the cosmopolitan, yet villagey, Stoke Newington. Rouge is a beautiful shop specialising in vintage and new furniture, ceramics, and decorative items for the home with an Asian flair - many brought directly from China, Vietnam and Thailand. With an emphasis on bold colours and simple forms, Rouge is the source for splashes of vivid hues and textures that complement any contemporary home design.

Inspired by her brother, who owns a similar shop in Brussels, Lei stepped away from her career in fashion and opened Rouge. She wanted to bring some inspirational items from her travels and reconnect to her Chinese upbringing. Lei named the business Rouge to evoke China's National colour but with a French influence in homage to her brother.

When choosing the items for the store, Lei looks for unusual elements laden with colour. "My aim is that when you enter the shop it offers a feast for the eyes that you will not see anywhere else."

The rustic, reclaimed furniture from rural China is particularly stunning and unique. These and other original items are what make Rouge so special and appreciated by the creative residents of Stoke Newington.

# THE THRIFTY STITCHER

CLAIRE-LOUISE HARDIE
UNIT 21, 4-6 SHELFORD PLACE, N16 9HS
MOB: 07779 255 087
@THRIFTYSTITCHER
INFO@THETHRIFTYSTITCHER.CO.UK
THETHRIFTYSTITCHER.CO.UK

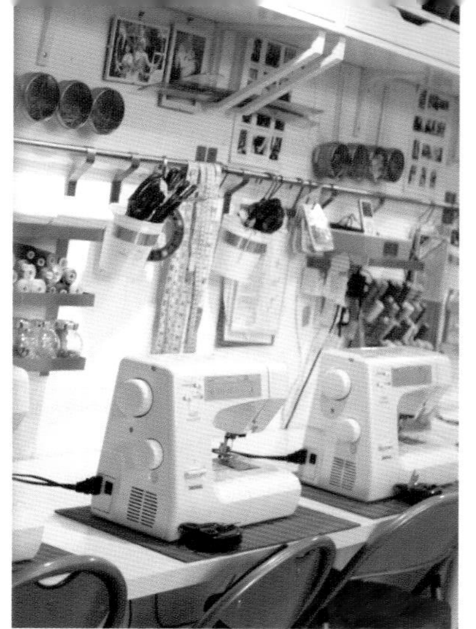

The Thrifty Stitcher offers friendly sewing classes in their bright studio in Stoke Newington. Founder and professional costumier Claire-Louise Hardie takes her experience as a dressmaker to the stars and sewing consultant to the BBC's "The Great British Sewing Bee", and shares her lifelong passion with students looking to find an outlet for their creative energy.

Claire-Louise's own threads unraveled after reading an article describing how no one was taught to sew anymore. "Believing that everyone could at least sew on a button, I was dismayed that so few people had this valuable life skill!"

Still maintaining her career as a Costumier, Claire-Louise takes her professional skills and passes the trade tips and tricks on to her students. Her most popular class is the one that started it all, an absolute beginners sewing day - teaching the basics and helping her students make the first stitch.

Always the resourceful seamstress, Claire-Louise appropriately named the business The Thrifty Stitcher, "It seemed to evoke a spirit of making and mending, and was a little quirky which suits both me and the business."

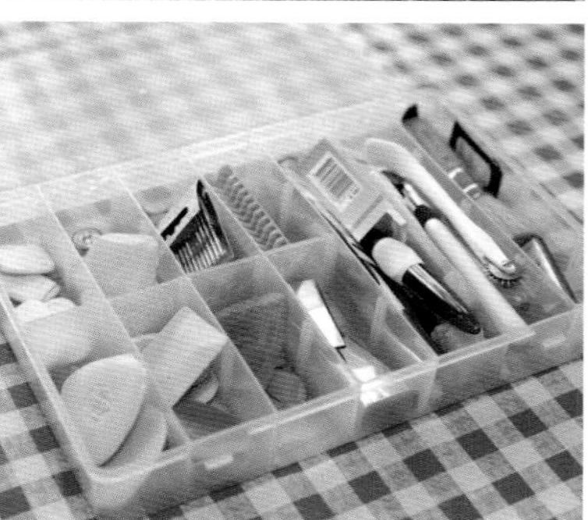

*photos by Milly Colley*

# EAST LONDON

An artistic hub, thriving with independent businesses, East London is the place to be. With eclectic areas, including Broadway Market and Victoria Park Village, there is an abundance of imagination to witness and inspiration to be found.

East London offers something special, combining the stricture of the City with the freedom of the artistic markets. Although it is still a little rough around the edges, this part of London is deserving of all its attention and praise. Thick with history, the area offers diversity, creativity, and vibrancy to any and all comers

I have included businesses in Spitalfields, Shoreditch, Broadway Market, Victoria Park Village, and the City to give you a peak at some of the variety of East London.

# THE MERCANTILE

DEBRA MCCANN
17 LAMB ST, E1 6EA
TEL: 020 7377 8926
@MERCANTILELDN
INFO@THEMERCANTILELONDON.COM
THEMERCANTILELONDON.COM

Nestled in the heart of East London, Spitalfields, The Mercantile is an eclectic boutique founded by Debra McCann. With a vintage vibe yet filled with contemporary collections, this truly independent shop takes the word to heart.

During her travels abroad, Debra fell in love with the many lifestyle boutiques she encountered and was impressed by the unique artisan products they sold. Inspired to offer artisan merchandise herself, Debra began sourcing and selling unique pieces that had both integrity and value.

Starting with a pop-up store, Debra grew a following of happy customers demanding more, leading to the now permanent location. Although they have recently launched an online store, Debra is proud to remain on the high street and encourages her customers to visit in person.

"Come meet us, try lots on, stroke the dog, smell the candles, and generally enjoy Mercantile and the community of Spitalfields."

Always taking on new and unknown designers, The Mercantile is constantly refreshed, and customers are spoilt for choice with the jewellery, apothecary, footwear, accessories, and luxury pieces that fill this one-of-a-kind shop.

*photos by Milly Colley*

Belinda Hay
Style Me Vintage
Easy step-by-step techniques for creating classic hairstyles
hair

*photos by Milly Colley*

# THE PAINTED LADY

BELINDA HAY
65 REDCHURCH STREET, E2 7DJ
TEL: 020 7729 2154
@MISSBELINDAHAY
INFO@THEPAINTEDLADYLONDON.COM
THEPAINTEDLADYLONDON.COM

The Painted Lady is tucked away on the artsy Redchurch Street, a perfect location for this quirky hair, makeup, and nail salon. Created by Belinda Hay aka The Painted Lady (and you can see why), the vintage inspired salon specialises in reproducing iconic looks from a bygone era of silver screen beauties.

"I have a passion for all things vintage and old fashioned values. I wanted to create an unassuming, friendly salon where people want to come and have their hair done and not feel self-conscious."

Using traditional hairstyling skills, Belinda and her team of stylists are trained in old fashioned and contemporary techniques. They are often found at vintage themed events in and around London, "victory rolling and building towering beehives". The primping and preening continues at the salon, which is host to many hen parties and retro styling nights.

Although the stylists are fully capable of creating a look worthy of any catwalk or Vogue magazine, The Painted Lady's loyal regulars often just enjoy the relaxed atmosphere while they sip Prosecco from a tea cup and get their hair, nails or makeup done.

# FABRICATIONS

BARLEY MASSEY
7 BROADWAY MARKET, E8 4PH
TEL: 020 7275 8043
BARLEY@FABRICATIONS1.CO.UK
FABRICATIONS1.CO.UK

Fabrications was founded in 2000 by textile designer-maker Barley Massey. Dedicated to contemporary textile practise and design, this independent gallery, shop, and studio is a leader in upcycling and eco-design.

One of the first businesses to move into Broadway market, Fabrications has hosted numerous exhibitions, promoted and sold work by over 200 local artists and designers, offered crafty workshops, and been featured at events across London.

After discovering Broadway Market in the late nineties, when the area was mostly boarded up shops, Barley recognised the strong sense of community and creativity in the area. When the council was encouraging creatives and local business to re-energise the empty shops, Barley seized the opportunity. "I felt at home here, it was full of potential, a fertile ground for sewing some positive seeds!"

In 2011, Barley created The Imaginarium, a craft space for classes at the back of the shop. She focuses on upcycling local business waste into beautiful and useful items and inspiring social and environmental change. Barley's brand is a reflection of her strong ecological and social ethos, as seen in one of her more popular products, the 'Rethink Rubbish' craft kit. These kits give the tools and supplies to teach people how to make fascinators, rosettes and phone cases - showing everyone there is more to "rubbish".

*photos by Milly Colley*

rethink rubbish
barley massey
sustainable
gift wrapping
HACKNEY BOROUGH COUNC
Nº7
BROADWAY
MARKET
E8
Fabrications

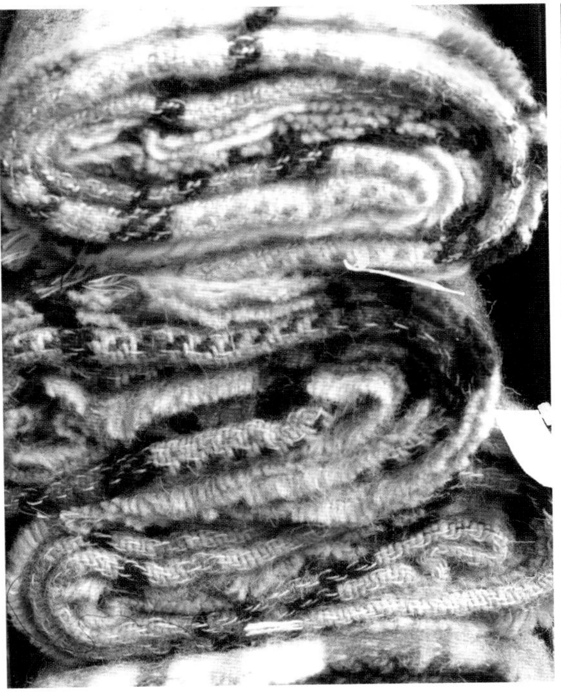

faithsolo

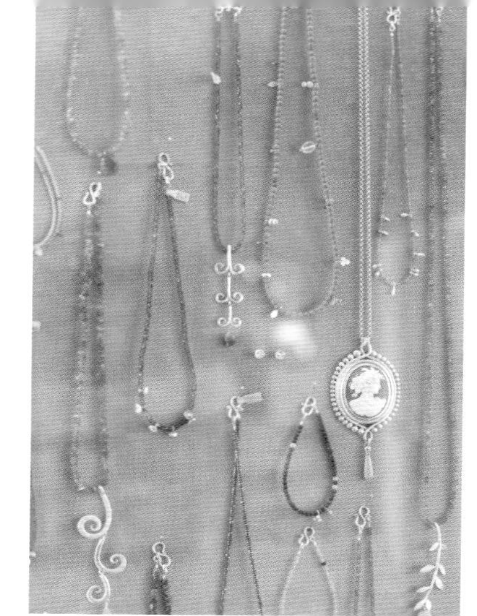

# BRANCH ON THE PARK

JULIA COOK
227 VICTORIA PARK ROAD, E9 7HD
TEL: 020 8533 7977
@BRANCHONTHEPARK
JULIA@BRANCHONTHEPARK.CO.UK
BRANCHONTHEPARK.CO.UK

Branch on the Park is a treasure trove filled with gems, beads, and precious metals, nestled in the small yet diverse village of Victoria Park. Opened by goldsmith Julia Cook in June 2010, this unique shop sells a collection of Julia's own designs as well as featuring collections from other independent jewellers, painters and photographers.

*photos by Milly Colley*

A passionate jeweller with over 20 years of experience, Julia demonstrates her skills by working on-site giving, her customers a behind-the-scenes look at her creativity in action. She takes on private commissions, working with customers to create, in her style, the perfect piece, including, but not limited to, engagement rings and wedding rings.

"Customers really enjoy having something made especially for them. Choosing stones, seeing the design and the piece develop throughout the making process"

With a keen eye for colour, Julia brightens her designs and her shop with coral, turquoise, and other dazzling precious and semi-precious stones. She also incorporates other elements from nature, which is always an inspiration for her, as seen in her gold and silver branches.The shop's name, Branch on the Park, is also an homage to nature and, of course, being practically inside Victoria Park it seemed a natural fit.

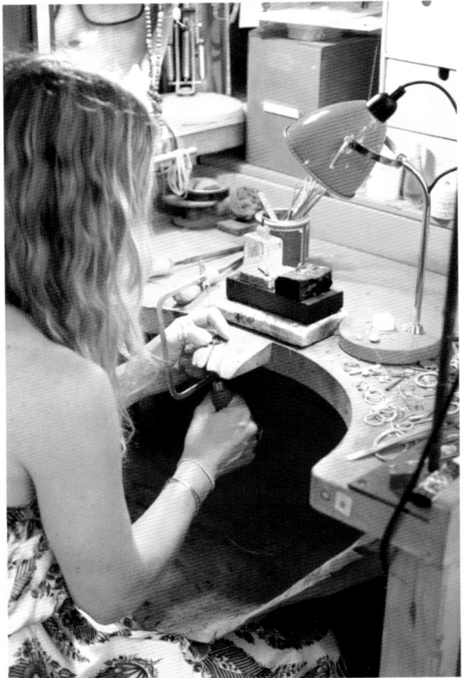

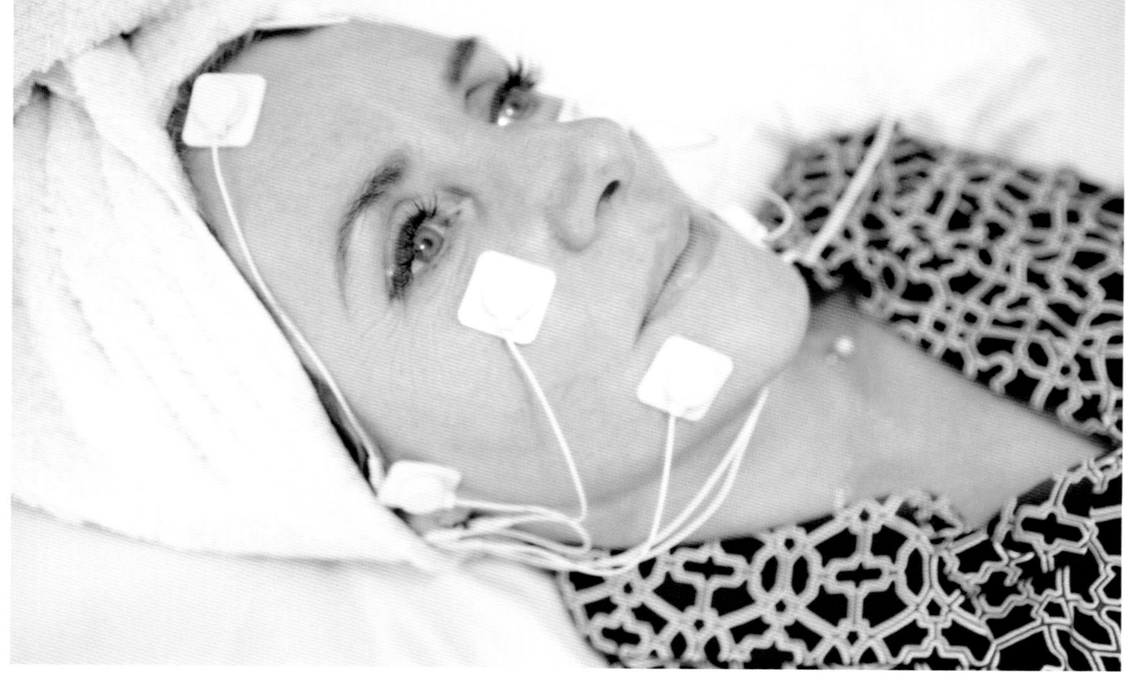

photos by Annie Armitage

# THE JUGGLING GODDESS

PAULA RUANE
LONGCROFT HOUSE, 2-8 VICTORIA AVE, EC2M 4NS
MOB: 07803 072 101
PAULA.RUANE@THEJUGGLINGGODDESS.COM
THEJUGGLINGGODDESS.COM

Paula Ruane at The Juggling Goddess employs advanced tools to release stress and pain using the science of bioenergetics - the energy flow through living systems. Helping women who do too much because they have to, while also trying to keep everyone else happy, Paula helps clients rebalance the past, deal with today, and create resilience for the future.

After experiencing a sequence of unwanted stressful events, Paula decided she needed to understand what caused stress and the ensuing health issues. "I was stressed, under pressure but didn't want drugs or talk therapy - I knew there must be another way."

After discovering bioenergetics and advanced technology based on traditional Chinese Medicine, Paula developed a unique programme which identifies and relieves the causes of stress and pain.

Stress shows on the face, which is why Beauty Bioenergetics has become Paula's most popular service. She simultaneously works throughout the whole energy system, revitalising the body and organs while removing the signs of ageing from the face. It is a non-invasive, relaxing yet re-energising and re-balancing treatment, turning the clock back, inside and out.

Paula based herself in the City to be closer to women she felt really needed her services. "Women in the City are in a highly competitive environment, which in itself is a significant cause of stress." Using a portfolio of powerful bio-feedback tools, Paula helps transform her clients physically, emotionally and mentally.

# SOUTH LONDON

Often described as leafy, South London has a wide range of sights and shops beyond the parks and parades. Ranging from multi-cultural and bustling Brixton to quaint and village-like Barnes, it has it all.

In South London, I discovered foodie favourites. I found London's first vegan bakery, a museum dedicated to chocolate, divine gelato, an exquisite gastropub, and an award-winning deli. The delicious delights will make your mouth water, but they are not the only treats in store.

There are a variety of businesses to help decorate yourself and your home or burn off the extra calories from a visit to any (or all) of the above.

You will find these businesses in Greenwich, East Dulwich, Clapham, Battersea, Barnes, Brixton, Kew, and Richmond-upon-Thames.

FRUITS OF THE FOREST
PEAR
Chocolate mousse cake
Squirrel cake

# BLACK VANILLA

SUSAN STRETCH
5 COLLEGE APPROACH, SE10 9HY
TEL: 020 8858 3283
@BLACKVANILLASE10
INFO@BLACK-VANILLA.COM
BLACK-VANILLA.COM

Susan Stretch set out to create an uncompromised, hand-crafted gelato and sorbetto using the finest, freshest ingredients. The result is Black Vanilla, offering award-winning flavours from chefs that bring a wealth of experience and obsession to every spoonful, something evident from the very first taste.

Following the ways of her grandmother, Susan and her husband read every label and are very careful about the food they give their two young daughters. "I was shocked to see that many of the ice creams being sold contained a large quantity of sweeteners and colourings. We decided to create a truly exquisite product that we felt comfortable feeding to our own children and that other parents could also have trust and confidence in."

Not just appreciated by children, the delectable and unique gelati and sorbetti are filled with quality ingredients including premium pistachios from Bronte and the finest hazelnuts from Piedmont. In their Moët Hennessy champagne bar is a selection of inventive alcoholic cocktails for an adult sorbetto or gelato treat.

Susan works tirelessly for her loyal customers who appreciate the time and effort it takes to create a high quality product. She knows first-hand that, as her father says, "success is one percent inspiration, ninety-nine percent perspiration".

*photos by Fanni Williams, except photo above by Joe Lord*

## ALSO AT

BLACKHEATH
32 TRANQUIL VALE, SE3 0AX
020 8852 0020

gelateria
black vanilla
black vanilla
black vanilla

MORA
SICILIAN BLOOD ORANGE
FRUITS OF THE FOREST
STRAWBERRY
MANGO
PEAR
POMEGRANATE
MOJITO

BIN END
VOUCHERS

photos by Charlotte Fielding

# THE PALMERSTON

REMI OLAJOYEGBE
91 LORDSHIP LANE, SE22 8EP
TEL: 020 8693 1629
@THEPALMERSTON
INFO@THEPALMERSTON.NET
THEPALMERSTON.NET

Serial entrepreneur Remi Olajoyegbe founded The Palmerston nearly a decade ago with her two business partners, Jamie and Paul. The trio sought to add something to East Dulwich that was missing - a bar and dining room serving a bold and ambitious modern British menu, a place with great food and great atmosphere.

Now with a number of awards under their belts and a loyal following of locals and foodies from far and wide, The Palmerston has become core to the, now bustling, High Street, a long way from its humble beginnings as an old-style British Pub.

The team takes full advantage of their prime location and has very recently developed a private dining area upstairs. They are working to restore the building inch by inch, from the ground to the roof.

The heart of The Palmerston is the food. With an ever changing menu to take advantage of seasonal excellence, there is something to please anyone's palate.

Speaking from her many experiences, Remi's advice to other entrepreneurs is clear. "Doing things that are different takes vision and ongoing commitment, make your experience the best it can be, know your audience and go for it!"

SONY

*photos by On Patisserie*

# ON PATISSERIE & ON COOKERY CLUB

LORETTA LIU
UNIT 4 NORTH ST MEWS
97 NORTH STREET, SW4 0HF
MOB: 07789 818 477
INFO@ONCAFE.CO.UK
ONCAFE.CO.UK

Encouraging London's devotion to French pastries, particulary macarons, Loretta Liu opened On Patisserie in 2010 and then the Cookery Club in 2011. With a love for classical French pastries, Loretta updated the delicious treats with inspiration from her heritage by adding the best of Asian flavours, style and elegance.

"We only use top quality ingredients and do not let our products taste solely of sugar. There are so many different flavours in the world and we like our customers to be able to taste and appreciate them."

Loretta takes great care at every stage of her baking, from crafting the flavours to delicately decorating each dessert. She draws on her vast experience and her skills learned while working with Michelin-starred chefs, studying at Valrhorna Chocolate School, and training in French cooking with experts including Pierre Gagnaire, Frederic Bau, and Alain Ducasse.

Now sharing her expertise with students in the Cookery Club, Loretta and her team of pastry chefs show the science behind making macarons. Students learn step-by-step the intricacies behind these famously tricky pastries. If beginner's macarons are too easy, intrepid bakers can try the Advanced Macarons, Trendy Eclairs and Croquembouche classes.

# DANDELION

KATE SAWYER & CLAIRE BATEMAN
120 NORTHCOTE ROAD, SW11 6QU
TEL: 020 7350 0902
@DANDELION120
DANDELIONONLINE.CO.UK

Dandelion is a charming and welcoming natural health store in the heart of Battersea's Northcote Road. Established in 1989, the current owners (Kate Sawyer, actress, and Claire Bateman, nutritionist and massage therapist) bought the store in 2008 after working there as part-timers for many years.

photos by Fanni Williams

"When the previous owner offered us the opportunity to buy the shop we both jumped at the chance to work together on something we are so passionate about."

It's that passion, with the encouragement and trust of the previous owner, that helped Kate and Claire update the store and refresh the character of the independent health food shop. With a dizzying variety of products, from luxurious face creams to simple natural oils, and their delectable lunches at the take-away counter, they take pride in offering something for anyone on the journey to better health!

The pair work hard to live up to their mission statement "health for everybody", proudly declared on the shop sign. "We love empowering people who are taking steps to improve their lives through lifestyle and diet." says Kate, "There is always an expert on hand to give advice, whether your question is about a health concern, a supplement, a new face cream or how to cook your rice!"

Dandelion
DETOX SALAD
ALAD: PAC-CHOI, CARROT, BEETROOT, CUCUMBER, ALFALFA, RED PEPPERS, SUNFLOWER SEEDS
RESSING: OLIVE OIL, LEMON JUICE, GARLIC, CAYENNE PEPPER, BLACK PEPPRER, BASIL
Dandelion
BEAN, PEPPER & SESAME SALAD
SALAD: GREEN BEANS, RED PEPPERS, GREEN OLIVES, SESAME SEEDS
DRESSING: OLIVE OIL, BRAGGS LIQUID AMINO ACIDS, LEMON JUICE, HONEGAR, WHOLEGRAIN MUSTARD, HERBEMARE, PEPPER
Dandelion
QUIONA SALAD

MUSHROOMS
6.72/kg
TOMATOES
£5.54/kg

photos by Annie Armitage

# LUMA

ALISON SATASI
98 CHURCH ROAD, SW13 0DQ
TEL: 020 8748 2264
ALISON@LUMADIRECT.COM
LUMADIRECT.COM

Alison Satasi fills her inspiring homewares shop 'Luma', nestled in leafy Barnes, with handcrafted, ethical and ecological items. Her carefully sourced collection of beautiful and unusual finds includes vintage fabric quilts, stunning hand-embroidered cushions, recycled wood frames, divine home fragrances, and one-off vintage furniture pieces.

Alison has a life-long passion for textiles. "Even as a teenager I came home from foreign holidays with suitcases full of local weaving and embroidery." In India and Peru she discovered wonderful local handicraft skills and admired the local traditions. After trekking through India, Alison left her banking career and created Luma to showcase hand-crafted discoveries.

Seven years later, Alison offers an abundance of amazing, unique textiles, many made exclusively for Luma, in addition to her vast collection of vintage and ethical items. Interior designers, stylists, and the design-conscious ethical shopper flock to the store in search of embroidered cushions, hand-woven blankets and pretty vintage fabric throws and bedspreads, not to mention Luma's own line of high quality organic and fairly traded bedding, which earned Vogue Magazine approval for eco-bedding.

Alison is continually in search of new and vintage treasures or creating new products with her suppliers, ensuring Luma offers new discoveries for all on every visit.

# THE CHOCOLATE MUSEUM

ISABELLE ALAYA
187 FERNDALE ROAD, SW9 8BA
MOB: 07723 434 235
@CHOCMUSEUMSW9
INFO@THECHOCOLATEMUSEUM.CO.UK
THECHOCOLATEMUSEUM.CO.UK

Chocolate aficionado Isabelle Alaya is a trained chocolatier and has a true appreciation for the delectable treat. After creating her own line of chocolates, Melange Chocolates, available in her Peckham shop, Isabelle created The Chocolate Museum to educate Londoners about the history of, and the process behind making, Chocolate.

Isabelle has filled her space in Brixton with historical advertisements from classic British chocolate brands, artefacts dating back to the 18th century, and details relating to the processing of chocolate.

Aside from historical items, The Chocolate Museum sells a wide range of artisan chocolates and serves delicious treats in their café. During her regular workshops held at the museum, Isabelle teaches adults, families, and school children how to make their own chocolate by experimenting with techniques and recipes.

"We infuse spices, herbs, fruit, flowers, seeds, tea & coffee into first grade Belgian chocolate to create unusual chocolate bars and unique flavour combinations."

Isabelle shares her love and passion for chocolate in every form - education, history, and bar!

*photos by Charlotte Fielding*

## ALSO AT

MELANGE CHOCOLATE SHOP
184 BELLENDEN ROAD, SE15 4BW
07722 650 711
THEMELANGE.COM

Ivory Coast
Ghana
Nigeria
Cameroons
Belgian Congo
Spanish Guinea
The Chief Cocoa Producing Countries of the World

OTHER BRANDS
Rowntree's Cocoa
Poulain

BLUEBERRY BLISS
CHOCOLATE VANILLA SPLIT
GLUTEN FREE
COSMOPOLITAN
Pina
GLUTEN
LEMON

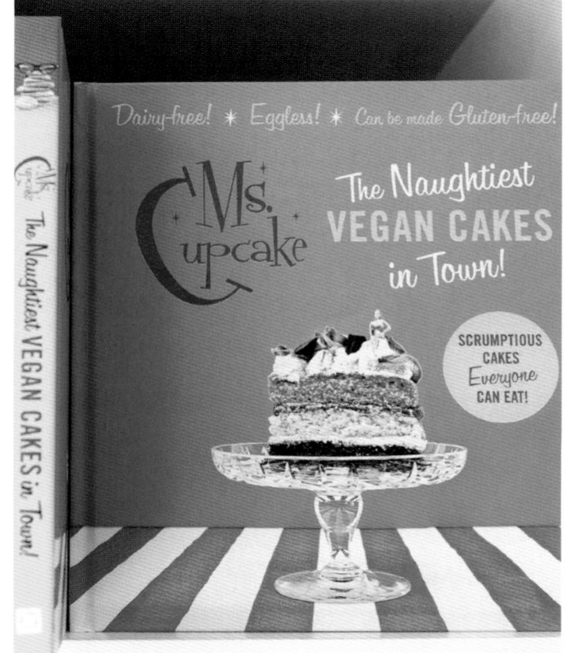
Dairy-free! ✶ Eggless! ✶ Can be made Gluten-free!
Ms. Cupcake
The Naughtiest VEGAN CAKES in Town!
SCRUMPTIOUS CAKES Everyone CAN EAT!
The Naughtiest VEGAN CAKES in Town!

# MS. CUPCAKE

MELLISSA MORGAN
408 COLDHARBOUR LANE, SW9 8LF
TEL: 020 7733 9438
@MSCUPCAKEUK
INFO@MSCUPCAKE.CO.UK
MSCUPCAKE.CO.UK

photos by Fanni Williams

Located in Brixton, the up and coming food centre of London, Ms. Cupcake, aka Mellissa Morgan, started London's first entirely vegan retail bakery. Offering over one hundred different flavours of cupcakes, a broad variety of layer cakes, cookies, cookie sandwiches, squares, and savoury items, Ms. Cupcake has something for everyone, regardless of their dietary restrictions.

A vegan herself, Mellissa went in search of the kind of cakes that she could (and wanted to) eat. Unable to find them, she set about making them herself. "We make decadent and delicious baked goods that all happen to be made without eggs or dairy. We also cater to gluten, soy and nut free diets."

Now attracting hungry customers from the local community, across the UK, and around the world, Ms. Cupcake has a cult following who enjoy her cakes, classes and books. "Our customers are extremely loyal and talk us up to everyone they know - we really are a community-led business."

Everything is handmade from scratch in the shop each day. Working from an open-plan kitchen, customers can watch the team baking and maybe even get a kiss and "hello sweetheart" from Ms. Cupcake herself.

photos by Charlotte Fielding

# ZITA ELZE FLOWERS

ZITA ELZE
287 SANDYCOMBE ROAD, TW9 3LU
TEL: 020 8940 0040
ZITA@ZITAELZE.COM
ZITAELZE.COM

Zita Elze brought her flair and magic to Kew in 2004, planting her store and all her lavish floral designs near the Royal Botanical Gardens and later adding prop hire and an international flower school, all while earning numerous awards including Best Wedding Florist 2012 and a silver-gilt medal at the Chelsea Flower Show.

Beginning her career in interior and garden design, Zita started to develop her signature style. Her individual technique creates exceptionally beautiful results and her remarkable attention to detail in the very delicate work creates an impactful, often emotional response.

A favourite of many brides, and one of the few florists to be recommended by Kew Gardens, Zita's flowers can be admired at many weddings. She has an extraordinary talent for realising a bride's vision and interpreting their thoughts and emotions through floral design. Her customers come to her for beauty and inspiration, such as her one-of-a-kind wedding gowns made of flowers, leaves and grasses.

Long before Zita began her career, she remembers passing a beautiful flower shop in Paris, owned by Christian Tortu - "a designer who gave the French floral design industry a real boost". Years later she began designing, but the shop left a lasting impact on her. Nowadays, she herself is a source of inspiration, not only through her floral creations, but through training aspiring floral designers of the future at Zita Elze Design Academy.

TIVOLI
A. V.
RUE SAINT-HONORÉ
A. V.
PARIS
STOCKHOLM
A. V.
PARIS
RUE SAINT-HONORÉ
A. V.

# HIGHLIGHT
# RICHMOND-UPON-THAMES

"Richmond is blessed with so many wonderful independent businesses, shops, cafes and restaurants that it deserves to also have a unique exercise venue! Barreworks is very much at home nestled in the beauty of this leafy, London suburb."

VICKI ANSTEY, OWNER OF BAREEWORKS

"I feel Richmond has a lovely selection and balance of independent boutique retailers and established High street brands.The location is small and friendly with the beautiful Richmond park and River Thames that take your breath away."

SARAH MAY MARSHALL, OWNER OF SARAH MAY JEWELLERY

Richmond is often considered one of the most attractive towns in London. With beautiful Royal parks, the River Thames, theatres, museums, galleries, and a town centre bursting with shops and restaurants, Richmond rivals anywhere in London.

Unlike many modern towns, Richmond has historic cobbled lanes and alleyways filled with exciting finds. It boasts an abundance of riverside cafes and bars which are perfect to relax by and enjoy a drink. Active visitors can enjoy a walk through Richmond Park - a true escape from the bustle of London.

# THE ALBERTS DELI

CATHY-SUE HOPE & JANICE TIMOTHY
2 WORPLE WAY, TW10 6DF
TEL: 020 8617 3029
@THEALBERTSDELI
INFO@THEALBERTSDELI.COM
THEALBERTSDELI.COM

Tucked away amongst charming Victorian terraces, The Alberts Deli, in The Alberts Richmond, is a delightful find for both locals and the hungry passer-by. The shop is filled with fresh, homemade food, offers fabulous cooked breakfasts, made to order sandwiches, and is the perfect place to pick up a gourmet goody for any reason.

Founded by Cathy-Sue Hope and her long-time friend Janice Timothy, The Alberts Deli brings their shared passion for food to the public. With lots of experience working in restaurants and Janice's insight from owning The Grove Park Deli (page 72), the duo saw taking joint ownership of The Alberts Deli in 2008 as something that was meant to be. "We were told about the shop by one of our French suppliers who had heard it was for sale and told us to see it. One look at the original art nouveau Parisian shop front and we were sold!"

Janice and Cathy-Sue now feed the local community of residents and workers tasty meals, snacks, and the famed Full Alberts Breakfast - Wick's Manor sausages and bacon, free range Organic eggs from Norfolk, delicious bread from Millers Bakery, roasted vine tomato, and mushrooms cooked in lashings of butter. The delectable tastes from The Alberts Deli can also be had further afield at private events through their London-Wide catering services.

*photos by Annie Armitage*

## ALSO AT

GROVE PARK DELI
22 FAUCONBERG ROAD, W4 3JY
TEL: 020 8995 8219
GROVEPARKDELI.COM

Chocolate Mousse cake (gluten free) £1.50
Squirrel cake apple, carrot, nuts & seeds £2.25
TRIPLE Choc £2.50

NEW SANDWICH MENU
try one of our tasty new fillings!

photos by Fanni Williams; prev page bottom by Jennalise Kassanis

# BARREWORKS

VICKI ANSTEY
VESTRY HOUSE, 21 PARADISE ROAD, TW9 1SA
TEL: 020 8940 5746
@BODYOFADANCER
VICKI@BARREWORKS.CO.UK
BARREWORKS.CO.UK

Barreworks is an exercise studio dedicated to barre and ballet-based workouts, created by Vicki Anstey. With origins in Lotte Berk and New York City Ballet Methods, Vicki's unique classes give a low impact but high intensity, full body workout and rapid progress towards achieving the physique of a dancer.

With no previous dance experience and very little motivation to exercise in the past, Vicki turned her life around after discovering barre-based exercise. She was so inspired by the workout that she left her career in advertising, began training as a teacher and did things she never thought possible - like training with the New York City Ballet!

Now Vicki shares her passion for barre-based classes in her Richmond studio. Designed to be a haven, this clean, light space is welcoming and inspiring.

Inside, students join in the signature Barreworks WorkOut using the ballet barre as a basis for a complete body workout. Students looking for a variety of workouts can also join the Ballet, StretchOut and RunOut classes - all designed to complement the principle method while offering additional athletic ballet training, deep stretching or running skills, giving a cardio-vascular element to the exercise regime.

After just a few classes, many students are converts and attend the workouts regularly. Vicki is reminded daily how effective the method is by seeing the changes in her students and loves to see her classes bring so much enjoyment. "We are lucky to see the best of people - their enthusiasm and dedication is contagious!"

photos by Fanni Williams

# SARAH MAY JEWELLERY

SARAH MAY MARSHALL
14 HILL STREET, TW9 1TN
TEL: 020 8948 2888
@SMAYJEWELLERY
INFO@SARAHMAYJEWELLERY.COM
SARAHMAYJEWELLERY.COM

Sarah May Jewellery has become one of Richmond's best kept secrets as a destination to buy beautiful objects to wear. Owner, Sarah May Marshall, showcases collections of handmade jewellery from individual designer-makers alongside her own line. She works on-site, customising bespoke designs, repairing jewellery, or renewing unwanted, yet sentimental, pieces into rejuvenated wearable art.

Inspired by her mother, fellow artist and boutique owner, Pamela Marshall, Sarah has always had a fascination for jewellery. "I've been drawn to the twinkle and sparkle of jewels since I was a young girl and used to love riffling through my mother's and grandmother's jewellery boxes, eagerly searching for treasures."

Sarah's bespoke jewellery services and large selection of items are not the only inspiring elements of her boutique. She also has some collections from the Caribbean, where she began her journey in jewellery, under the mentorship of Trinidad's jewellery extraordinaire, Barbra Jardine.

After graduating from The Royal College of Art, Sarah started her career sharing a small studio workshop. Her experiences showcasing her creations helped her realise that she craved the interaction with clients. Her inviting shop in the heart of Richmond provides just that. "We are consistently developing friendships with our clients, creating a personal buying experience."

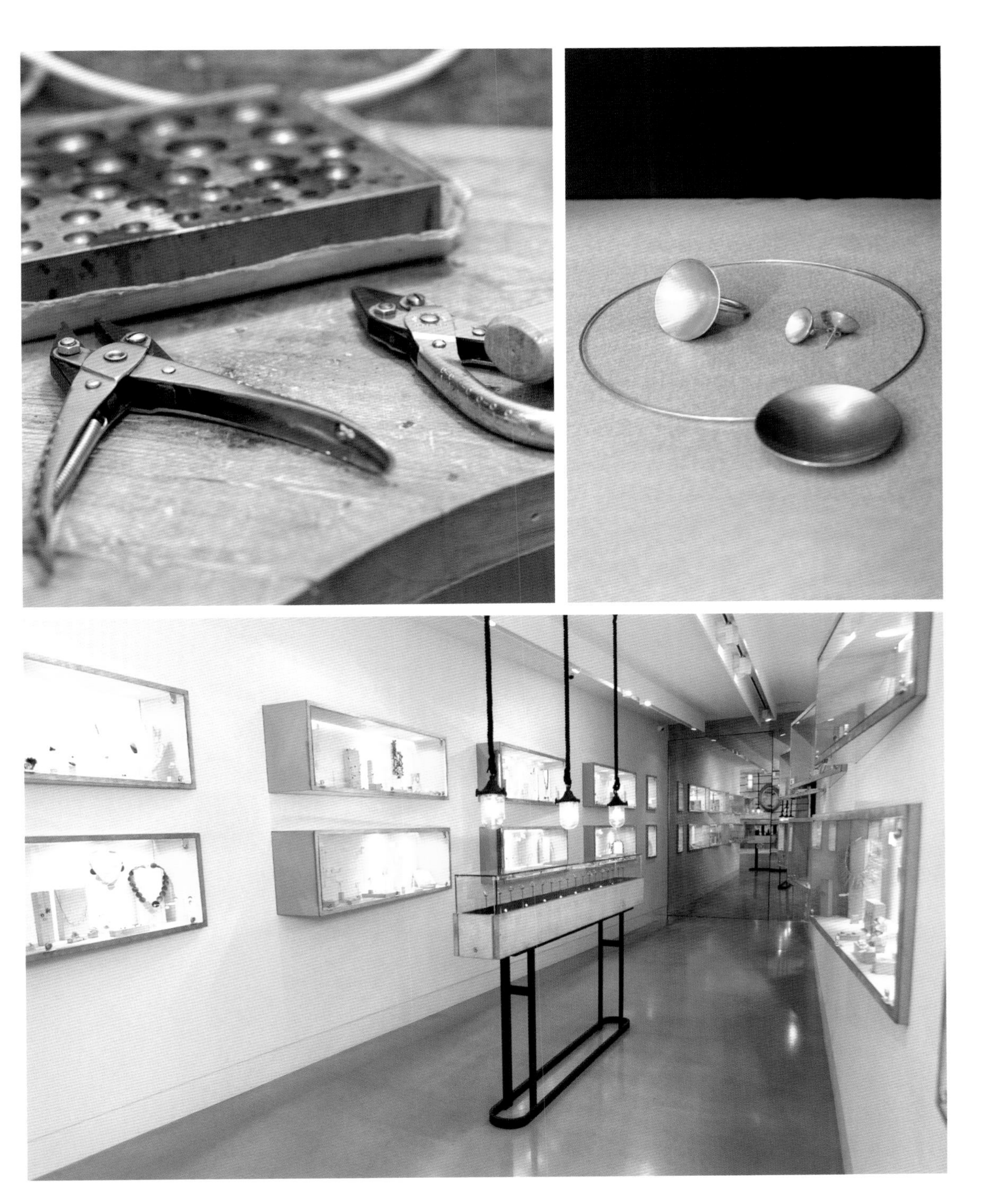

# LONDON-WIDE

In the London-wide section you will find the businesses beyond the villages. The women in this section bring their expertise to everyone across London - they can and will go anywhere. They help you get fit, get organised, plan your special occasions, design your home, entertain you, and make you laugh. They have all the skills and talents to broaden our minds and provide all the services that we depend on in our daily lives, and they bring it all to your door.

FUNNY WOMEN
MAIN AWARD

*photos by Annie Armitage*

# ANNIE ARMITAGE PHOTOGRAPHY

ANNIE ARMITAGE
MOB: 07711 391 919
@ANNIEGOLIGHTLY
ANNIE@ANNIEARMITAGE.COM
ANNIEARMITAGE.COM

Working with a wide range of customers from families to professionals, Annie Armitage, a leading photographer, puts people at ease during her photoshoots. From newborns to businessmen, Annie works with her subjects to reveal their sweetness and innocence, or their professionalism and affability, but she specialises in on-location photography that captures families enjoying moments together.

"I go to the client and work within their own environment, or we set the scene in a local park and I photograph them having fun together. The aim is to create lasting memories that can be shared through generations."

Annie brings out the best in people with her enthusiasm, initiative and creativity. She takes great care to make the experience unforgettable and personal. Her clients appreciate her attention to detail and can relate to Annie. "My customers are usually of a very creative nature, have strong family values and understand my quirkiness!!"

With a family heritage of entrepreneurs, Annie knew that it was her destiny to make her own way. "My advice to fellow creative entrepreneurs is to remember that to be successful, it is more about your business skill than your creativity."

# BUY:TIME

CLAIRE BRYNTESON
91-93 BUCKINGHAM PALACE ROAD, SW1W ORP
TEL: 020 3292 0566
@BUYTIMELONDON
INFO@BUY-TIME.CO.UK
BUY-TIME.CO.UK

Feeling overwhelmed with career, social and family commitments, founder Claire Brynteson knew there had to be a better way. In 2002 she created buy:time, the first business to make time a commodity and allow customers to buy it in "whatever sized bottle they need". Providing clients with a dedicated personal assistant able to help with the everyday tasks like household management and errand running to more complicated project management for entrepreneurs.

"We are all being challenged by the pace of life and seemingly struggling with similar things. The paperwork mountain, the never ending list of things to do, fix, find, organise, book, oversee. To have someone, the same person, to see things through from start to finish and to fight in our corner while they do it is so immensely valuable."

Each assistant offers a hands-on solution - they will travel with you or even travel for you if need be. Since busyness and business are different each week, you can even buy time on a Pay-As-You-Go basis.

Now with many years of experience, a skilled team of committed assistants, a flexible approach and the ability to work both remotely and on site, buy:time changes lives.

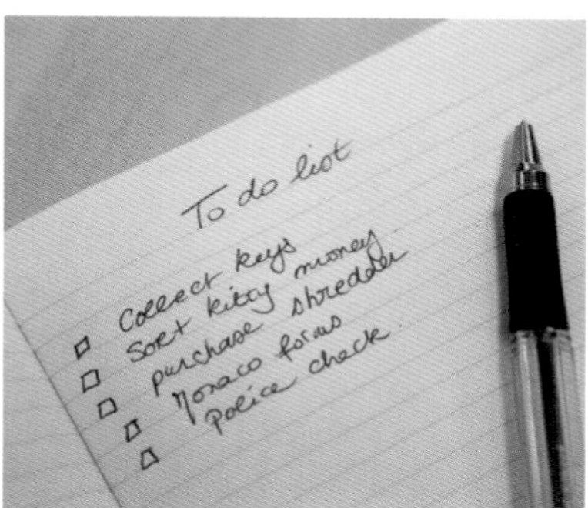


*photos by Annie Armitage*

*photos by Lucy Williams*

# CHARLENE HUTSEBAUT PERSONAL TRAINER & FITNESS ENTREPRENEUR

CHARLENE HUTSEBAUT
MOB: 07904 904 249
@POSITIVELYSLIM
CHARLENE@CHARLENEHUTSEBAUT.COM
CHARLENEHUTSEBAUT.COM

With a passion for wellbeing, Charlene Hutsebaut, personal trainer, brand ambassador, and fitness entrepreneur, has always loved feeling healthy, and she shares the tools to live this way with her clients. Her extensive career started at an early age and is the only one that Charlene ever saw herself doing. She completed her university degrees specialising in Personal Training and has spent 20 years guiding clients with her solid knowledge and experience.

Described by clients as a "real woman for real people", Charlene has a realistic body and outlook on life. Her goal is to help her clients learn to live healthily forever, not just for a few months.

Charlene works with clients one-on-one on nutrition, exercise, and lifestyle management. Her online membership, PositivelySlim.ning.com, is an extension of her real time work, through e-books, videos, work sheets and more.

An expert in the industry, Charlene also supports corporations in their quest for health and has worked with Huggies Diapers, The De-Stress Diet, Healthy Supplies, DNA Fit, and Siemens. Her valued advice is also often featured in a range of magazines, including Total Sports Nutrition and Woman, making her tips to better health accessible to all.

# CRANBERRY BLUE WEDDINGS & EVENTS

MELANIE HELEN
TEL: 01732 463 633
@CRANBERRYBWED
ENQUIRIES@CRANBERRYBLUEWEDDINGS.CO.UK
CRANBERRYBLUEWEDDINGS.CO.UK

*photos by Victoria Grech*

Cranberry Blue is a boutique consultancy, founded by Melanie Helen, specialising in the planning and creation of distinctive and elegant weddings across the UK and abroad. Providing meticulous attention to detail, an expert eye for design, exemplary service and striving for perfection, a wedding designed by Melanie will always delight.

Starting out her career in fashion and events, Melanie became very familiar with both style and organisation. After attending several weddings, she noticed that most were, sadly, both uninspiring and disorganised and felt that her skills would be perfectly aligned to create more aspirational events, better fitting the occasion.

"I always strive for perfection and love keeping ahead when it comes to new trends, be it reception ideas, colours and décor etc., and have the ability to adapt these to suit individuals."

Coming to what felt like a natural decision, Melanie realised she was meant to be a Wedding Planner. Working closely with each couple, she helps create their perfect day, exceeding their expectations and allowing them to relish in every moment without the stress that often accompanies planning weddings.

"Everything we do is on a bespoke basis and unique to each couple, so there aren't any set ways of working. It's about being flexible to our client's requirements, and they tell us how much they appreciate our personal approach."

THE KING
OF JAZZ
(1930)

# FLOURISH

KAREN DOWNES
MOB: 07714 616 359
KAREN@KARENLEEDOWNES.COM
TIMETOFLOURISH.CO.UK

Flourish is dedicated to women who have entered the second half of their life and want to live each day vibrantly and with meaning. Founded by Karen Downes, this online business provides inspiration, guidance, support, and products to help women navigate their way through the changes and challenges that come later in life.

At the age of 50, Karen had an epiphany,"I was not prepared for the dramatic changes that happened to my body and in my life. I wanted to create a new framework for this phase of life, for myself and other women, to provide support on all levels, to truly flourish in the second half of life. With the challenges and transitions we face, we can't always be happy, but we can always be our best selves.

"Flourish is a philosophy, an approach to life - it has been created in honour of life's irrepressible impulse to grow and thrive, to feel truly alive and to fulfil our potential."

A holistic approach to living well, Flourish is based on Karen's heartfelt connection to nature, her passion for nurturing, and her commitment to helping people find meaning and purpose in their lives. She guides her clients to positive living through events and adventures, and each product offered has been carefully chosen to invigorate and nourish the body, mind and spirit.

Using her experience as a holistic natural health care practitioner, a business consultant, an executive coach and from her own personal path to wellbeing, Karen helps others on their transformational journey.

"Luck is preparation
meets opportunity.
If you are prepared
and take the opportunities
that come your way,
your luck will be made."

MARCELLE SYMONS
*D&Me*

photos: this page and next page bottom by Grace Lightman; next page top by Amelia Wells

# FUNNY WOMEN

LYNNE PARKER
TEL: 020 8948 4444
@FUNNYWOMEN
LYNNE@FUNNYWOMEN.COM
FUNNYWOMEN.COM

Funny Women is the UK's leading community for female comedy, helping women to perform, write and do business with humour. Set up by Lynne Parker in 2002 the company produces live shows, the Funny Women Awards, runs workshops and provides training and coaching for women in their personal and business lives all the while keeping its community involved and informed through the lively editorially led website.

The creation of Funny Women came as a knee jerk reaction from Lynne, after a misogynistic male comedy promoter said "there aren't any funny women". She's spent 10 years getting her revenge and then some - inspired by the capacity women have for laughing about life and getting on with some of the most difficult things with humour and grace.

"Female comedy is my passion and I enjoy helping women to develop their capacity for humour to build their confidence and present themselves more powerfully."

To encourage more women into comedy, Funny Women runs training activities and workshops for performing and writing which encourage a storytelling, narrative approach. The workshops range from the introductory 'Stand Up to Stand Out' to advanced workshops and whole weekends for a more intensive learning experience. Not only do the workshops support women who want to perform comedy, they also attract professional business women who want to learn how to use humour to develop their presentation skills and boost self-confidence.

The annual Funny Women Awards celebrates and promotes women in comedy, and is widely recognised as the leading comedy competition for female performers, writers and originators attracting around 300 entries per year.

Believing in the existence of "feminine intuition", Lynne encourages aspiring female entrepreneurs to pursue any opportunity or gap in the market they believe they can fill. "Have the courage of your convictions, and remember that humour is vital to communication. It's very empowering to be funny."

# KAREN KENNABY

KAREN KENNABY
MOB: 07595 316 613
@KARENKENNABY
KAREN@KARENKENNABY.COM
KARENKENNABY.COM

Karen Kennaby is an Intuitive Food Coach. She helps women by introducing them to the best foods and the best way of eating to suit them as individuals. Karen's unique holistic approach incorporates her knowledge of food with an understanding of the mind, helping women discover their weight and body image issues. Her approach empowers her clients to look and feel their best - transforming all areas of their life.

Karen began her journey to becoming a Food Coach at the age of 17, when she trained as a chef. Taking her love for food and new culinary expertise, she then studied nutrition and how the mind works and brought it all together to create a powerful combination. "I initially rid myself of IBS symptoms and lost a stone, and when I knew I had created a winning formula I started to share it with as many people as possible."

Working with each client one-to-one, Karen begins by delving into the emotions surrounding food, discovering what has sabotaged her client's weight loss efforts in the past, their history and their vision. She supports her clients by providing quick and easy recipes, tutorials, eating plans, videos, and interviews.

"They come to me for weight loss or health reasons primarily and are delighted when they find the changes we make together take their whole life to a new level of enjoyment." A statement backed up by her numerous testimonials praising her results. Karen is often thanked for changing her client's lives through her support and encouragement - leaving them happier, more confident, and of course healthier.

“Building a successful
business takes time,
it won’t happen overnight.
But if you keep going
and work hard,
it will happen.”

MELANIE HELEN
*Cranberry Blue*

# ISABEL SMITH WEDDING DESIGN

ISABEL SMITH
TEL: 01628 810 231
MOB: 07815 131 576
@ISWEDDINGDESIGN
ISABEL@ISABELSMITHWEDDINGS.CO.UK
ISABELSMITHWEDDINGS.CO.UK

Isabel Smith works with couples from engagement to vows, helping them choose a wedding theme, select the perfect suppliers, and stay within their budget, ensuring they have the perfect wedding. "I specialise in helping my clients thoroughly enjoy the process of creating weddings which look fantastic, run smoothly and are remembered by their guests for all the right reasons."

Isabel's career as an in-house wedding coordinator was a means to an end. It allowed her to gain the experience and knowledge she needed to be able to offer something better. Isabel knew from the day she started she was in love with the idea of becoming a Wedding Planner and that her priorities lay with the clients and not the hotel.

Working tirelessly for couples who come to her for her expertise, Isabel feels personally invested in their day and knows that her attention to details contributes to the bigger picture, "two people making this amazing commitment in front of their family and friends".

*photos by Isabel Smith Wedding Design*

# MISS BALLOONIVERSE

NATALIE
MOB: 07958 399 238
@MSBALLOONIVERSE
NATALIE@MISSBALLOONIVERSE.CO.UK
MISSBALLOONIVERSE.CO.UK

Miss Ballooniverse adds a touch of glamour and heaps of fun to events. From children's parties to formal black tie events, Natalie's balloon art works in every varied age-group, language, and situation. "Seeing a new creation taking shape - or spotting one across a crowded room - is the ultimate ice-breaker and leveller."

An artistic entrepreneur from a young age - she sold paintings to her dad as a tot - Natalie knew that balloons were what she was looking for when she found them. She loved the colour, creativity and the opportunity to perform. Natalie took a somewhat forgotten art, combined it with her fifties-inspired flair and made balloon art glamorous.

Natalie twists balloon rings, fascinators, and bracelets for more conservative wearers, but can also sculpt an item deserving of Ascot or a Vegas audience. Adding a little pizzazz to the corporate environment, she also teaches others her balloon skills during team building events.

"Everyone knows children love balloons, but I love that people are learning that balloons can be elegant and sophisticated too. Of course, balloons bring out the big kid in everyone!"

# MISS NUTRITIONIST

ROSIE MILLEN
TEL: 020 7060 3163
@MS_NUTRITIONIST
ENQUIRIES@MISSNUTRITIONIST.COM
MISSNUTRITIONIST.COM

Rosie Millen, aka Miss Nutritionist, provides friendly one-to-one nutritional consultations, advising on healthy eating. She supports optimum health and wellness by inspiring others to achieve enhanced wellbeing. She offers advice on how to eat and feel better by adjusting diet and lifestyle and adding supplements.

Rosie was blown away when she learned more about the concept of the "power of food as medicine" and wanted to share that message with as many people as she can reach. "You really are what you eat. I want to help people to realize that as much as possible."

Inspired by Gillian McKeith's tenacity in the industry and her own passion about healthy eating, Rosie is determined to help people look and feel better. Providing advice that is specific to each individual through a tailored program, she helps people optimise energy levels, digestion, hormone balance, and weight management.

Starting her business immediately after she completed her training, Rosie knows the challenges that face aspiring entrepreneurs. "Don't give up. Remember why it is that you are doing what you are doing. Always follow your gut. It's all you have when things are tough."

“Make sure your business has something to set it apart from others and hold on to that uniqueness as the business grows.”
VICKY ANSTEY
*Barreworks*

Proposed Annexe to Existing
Original drawn by: Simon De Grussa
NETGEAR
MADE IN CHINA
NTA Projects inc. Atelier 16 chartered architects
3 Drayton Park, 1st Floor Suite, Highbury, London N5 1NU

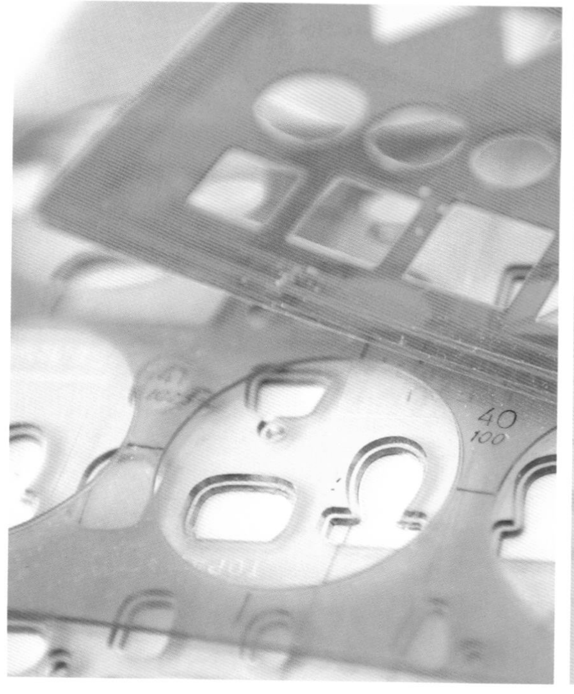
40
100

BEDROOM

photos by Lucy Wiliams

# NTA16 ARCHITECTS

IOLANDA COSTIDE, AADIPL RIBA FACC
TEL: 020 7609 9888
@NTA16ARCHITECTS
CONTACT@NTA16ARCHITECTS.CO.UK
NTA16ARCHITECTS.CO.UK

With the motto "Good Design is Good Business", Iolanda Costide and her team at NTA16 architects bring a fresh approach to the male-dominated industry of construction. Covering all aspects of the practice from residential to mixed developments, NTA16 architects are able to take on any project. "We are trained to see the 'bigger picture'; we create total environments, interior and exterior, which are pleasing and functional."

Inspired by a passion for design and encouraged by senior mentors while studying at the Federal Politechnic Lausanne and later the Architectural Association in London, Iolanda's goal was to, one-day, own her own practice. She longed for freedom of choice and the ability to take action within her projects.

Now leading her team, Iolanda uses a collaborative approach when working with clients, including them from the early design stages. She remains highly involved from start to finish, and her extensive knowledge gives clients confidence in the team. "We are good designers and have long term experience in practice, giving clients the necessary peace of mind in a process which can be stifling and complex."

Iolanda's enthusiasm about each job is shown in her exemplary attention to detail throughout development and her joy upon completion. "There is no greater satisfaction than starting a project, going through the design process and then witnessing the dream realised."

photos by Ohlala Macarons

# OHLALA MACARONS

MEREDITH O'SHAUGHNESSY
MOB: 07958 354 934
@OHLALAMACARONS
BOOKINGS@OHLALA-MACARONS.COM
OHLALA-MACARONS.COM

Created by Meredith O'Shaughnessy, Ohlala Macarons is the first macaron and martini making workshop in the UK, a workshop that unveils the secrets of how to bake the perfect macaron, followed by the opportunity to get hands on with expert mixologists, behind the bar, mixing and shaking delicious martinis - the ideal combination of education and pleasure, a true feast for the senses.

A lover of macarons after a visit to Paris, Meredith grew frustrated with the complexity of making these delicate treats. "Although I've baked all my life, when I came to giving macarons a go I found the information in all the cookery books really confusing, so once I mastered their delights I wanted to share the skills I had developed with others."

During the workshops, Meredith de-bunks the myths of macarons. She makes cooking fun and accessible, ensuring that everything used is something easily found in a home kitchen. Adding martinis to the classes puts a twist of "fun and frivolity" to the typical cooking class and makes the afternoon truly an occasion.

Meredith's events are a perfect way to spend an afternoon with friends. Many brides-to-be have also enjoyed the afternoon antics. With an unlimited macarons and martinis policy, everyone leaves happy and with a new appreciation for the delicate dessert and classic cocktail.

# ORGANISED & SIMPLE

PATTY CRUZ-FOUCHARD
MOB: 07818 830 917
PATTY@ORGANISEDANDSIMPLE.COM
ORGANISEDANDSIMPLE.COM

*photos: this page by Jason Cox; next page by Tangyan, Shutterstock.com*

For most, getting organised is a daunting task. The idea of sorting clutter makes us cringe, but for Patty Cruz-Fouchard it's a passion. A professionally certified organising company, Organised & Simple specialises in a variety of areas, from decluttering rooms to teaching how to deal with paper in an efficient and straightforward way. Patty provides a plethora of tools helping restore order, calm and simplicity to daily life.

After 15 years in finance, Patty had a moment of clarity and discovered her passion. "I realised I was drawn to, and enjoyed, organising friends, family, my home, and any project that came along."

Now working closely with many clients and covering all sorts of challenges, Patty begins each project with an (unsurprisingly) detailed assessment. Each solution is customised to give her clients structure, allowing them to take control of their time and priorities. "The solutions are long lasting. I teach my clients routines and systems to stay organised."

An advocate for order, Patty has helped her clients become less stressed and given them more time to do the things that matter to them; ultimately improving the quality of life - all by giving them simple solutions to stay organised!

# PARTNERS IN STYLE

CLAUDIA DE BIASI & MICHELE LANGENBRINCK
MOB: 07877 216 465
STUDIO@PARTNERSINSTYLE.CO.UK
PARTNERSINSTYLE.CO.UK

*photos by Annie Armitage*

Partners in Style, Claudia de Biasi and Michele Langenbrinck, offer a comprehensive, individualised experience to styling; everything is covered, from clearing out wardrobes, to assembling a series of new looks for any occasion, to creating a lookbook for later reference. Together they ensure their clients can dress with confidence.

Inspired by each other, Claudia and Michele are both enthusiastic about discovering exciting new clothes, shoes and accessories not found on the high street and helping clients look their best. Sharing the same approach to clothes, style, and work, they are a true partnership and complement each other's approach, maximizing the service to each client.

"You don't see many stylists or companies that employ two people per client at once, so the fact that we devote twice the manpower to each person makes us a bit different and far more efficient than we would be alone."

The pair are influenced by and pay attention to current trends, but they focus on the individual style that is right for each client. They have such a deep understanding that they often shop without the client being present. "We are able to tell after a discussion and meeting with our clients what they need, and can shop alone then come back to the client with items that we know will work."

During trips abroad, they often return laden with unique products including a new line of beautiful shoes from Italy and Spain, jewellery from Greece and Brazil, and other hand-picked pieces from across the world, exclusively for their clients.

# PT MOLLIE

MOLLIE MILLINGTON
MOB: 07816 068 060
@PTMOLLIE
MOLLIE@PTMOLLIE.COM
PTMOLLIE.COM

*photos by Fanni Wiliams, portrait by PT Mollie*

A personal trainer and wellness coach, Mollie Millington works with clients to help them achieve health and happiness through exercise, work-life balance and proper nutrition. Her services include in-person and online personal training (with 8-week virtual training groups) and nutritional counselling. Mollie's expertise has also been shared through fitness articles in Cosmopolitan, So Feminine, Women's Health and other leading magazines.

Mollie decided to become a personal trainer after successfully helping a friend achieve her fitness goals. Having personal experience of improving her fitness and general health, she relates to clients' struggles and helps identify solutions. Personal training is something Mollie enjoys. "Working with clients and seeing them realise goals and achieve what they previously thought impossible is an amazing experience that in turn motivates me."

Mollie respects her clients because they have already shown courage and ambition in approaching her in the first place. She sets her clients "SMART" goals (specific, measurable, achievable, relevant, and time-bound), supporting and encouraging them while they work towards achieving them. After finding their appropriate balance "at home, in the office, at the dinner table, and at the gym", Mollie assists her clients in maintaining this balance for the future.

Mollie values the positive effect of deriving support from others, advising fellow or aspiring entrepreneurs to "find a good mentor and a good accountant"... and of course, not to forget the importance of maintaining their good health at the same time!

# THE PURE PACKAGE

JENNIFER IRVINE
TEL: 08456 123 888
@PUREPACKAGE
INFO@PUREPACKAGE.COM
PUREPACKAGE.COM

photos by The Pure Package

The Pure Package, and its country-wide sister brand Balance Box, help clients meet their health goals whilst eating fresh, ethically sourced, bespoke meals. Jennifer Irvine and her team deliver customised packages to each client, filled with a delicious daily menu of breakfast, lunch and dinner alongside healthy snacks.

Jennifer, the pioneer of the industry, started The Pure Package from her own kitchen. She worked hard to educate people on the value of healthy food and showed them how easy it can be to include it as a regular part of their lives.

"Healthy food should taste great! Clients look forward to receiving their meals every day to see what's next on the menu. Popular dishes include free-range jerk chicken with coconut - delicious and healthy!"

Now nourishing the country, along with celebrities including Hugh Jackman, Julian McDonald and Matthew Williamson, Jennifer delivers packages of delectable meals that also meet nutritional needs. Clients eat the optimum amount of essential fats, protein, carbohydrates, fibre, fruit, and vegetables to support their goals - chosen from a wide range of programmes including general healthy eating, weight loss and pre- and post-baby nutrition.

With the kitchen strategically located next to New Covent Garden Market, Jennifer and her chefs have access to limitless fresh ingredients, getting her as close to a farm as central London can offer. Jennifer has come a long way from her childhood beginning - selling eggs from her family farm in West Cork, Ireland to local restaurants and markets, but still stands behind the core of the business - providing people with good quality food!

**ALSO AT** BALANCE BOX TEL: 03331 230 818 HELLO@BALANCEBOX.COM BALANCEBOX.COM

tempting!
Thursday
balance box

THE PURE PACKAGE
THE PURE PACKAGE

# RACHELLE'S

RACHEL HILL
TEL: 020 8764 3327
MOB: 07958 714 672
RACHEL@RACHELLES.CO.UK
RACHELLES.CO.UK

With a flair for design and a love for delicious cakes, Rachel Hill began her business after the economic downturn. Previously working as an Art Director and Designer (for TV and film), Rachel took her artistic talent, mixed it with baking skills, hard work and perseverance to create a successful cake company.

Rachelle's specialises in creating gorgeous bespoke cakes and confections for weddings, parties and special occasions. From novelty cakes to cake pops to large elegant tiered cakes, Rachel pours love and care into every delicious detail.

"I am inspired every day by my work. Not only can I continue to pursue my love of design, but I can bake and create something that both looks wonderful and tastes wonderful!"

She follows trends in fashion and interior design and works closely with her clients to customise her creations to suit them perfectly. Rachel finds inspiration in Wedding invitations, stationary, or themes, giving her clients something unique and bespoke - a cake that will never be forgotten.

Loved by her clients, as seen in her many testimonials, Rachel always goes the extra mile and never shy's from hard work. "Because I love doing it so much, it feels less like a job and more like hobby that I get paid to do! Nothing is too much trouble, and to me my goal is to deliver ultimate perfection."

*photos by Annie Armitage*

Rachelle's
BEAUTIFUL BESPOKE CAKES

Eat me

"Dare to hope, dare to dream,
do not doubt yourself;
work hard."
IOLANDA COSTIDE
NTA16 architects

# RHONA CLEWS PERSONAL DEVELOPMENT & CHANGE EXPERT

RHONA CLEWS
MOB: 07870 668 325
RHONA@RHONACLEWS.CO.UK
RHONACLEWS.CO.UK

A self-confessed self-help junky as a teenager, Rhona Clews is now a seasoned personal development and change expert with 18 years experience and a background in Clinical Psychology. She specialises in health, wealth, confidence, and supporting people as they navigate change. She is also passionate about helping clients recover from trauma and recoup from addiction.

"Whilst the subjects I work with are weighty, I feel lightness and joy are central to my approach."

Rhona's own commitment to personal development directly informs her work - she tries the latest techniques on herself and, through this first-hand testing, identifies the most effective.

"From my experience, traditional approaches have only brought us so far. Yes, change does begin with knowledge and awareness, but often people get stuck in the 'knowing' stage, repeating the same behaviours despite knowing better! My work is about transforming this awareness into actual behaviour change and delivering long-lasting, tangible results."

Having expertise in a range of therapies to teaching standard, Rhona is a renowned teacher as well as practitioner. As she supports each client to release what is blocking them in the present, she simultaneously passes on skills and resources in each session, creating a solid foundation of self care, independence and freedom for the future.

"When we are given the right tools, we all flourish. It doesn't matter how hard or complex things have become with the right support and environment for empowerment, we get results. My clients leave both lighter and better prepared for any challenges, with a deeper and more loving relationship with themselves."

# SCARLETT

SALLI GLOVER
MOB 07963 962 640
@WEARESCARLETT
SALLI@WEARESCARLETT.COM
WEARESCARLETT.COM

Scarlett is a three-month programme of high-impact training and mentoring for women on a mission. The programme works by tapping into your Big Vision, taking on powerful daily habits that align your daily actions to your bigger goals and by being supported with one-to-one coaching to keep you on track. Led by Salli Glover, they are also a tribe of extraordinary women who support one another through an online community every single day... it's amazing what miracles happen with that level of focused support and accountability!

Salli believes that women are the solution to our twenty-first century challenges and that the future is definitely female. Through Scarlett, Salli helps women who have already identified what they want out of life gain access to the support they need, including knowledge and people. Having already trained with leading personal and professional organisations and coaching providers, she has created a programme which specifically supports women, and one which will continue to bring about a positive effect well into the future.

The members of Scarlett are highly motivated women who are on a mission and their calibre and quality add value to the programme. "These are real, raw, open and normal women who are playing a bigger game in life - and are giving each other a leg up along the way!"

photos by Six Dinners Later

# SIX DINNERS LATER

JANEY DE NORDWALL & REMI OLAJOYEGBE
TEL: 020 7613 1840
@SIXDINNERSLATER
INFO@SIXDINNERSLATER.COM
SIXDINNERSLATER.COM

Craving some interaction off-line, Janey de Nordwall and Remi Olajoyegbe created Six Dinners Later to give people a new way to meet. The social network and dining club introduces you to twenty-five new people over a round of six dinner parties, allowing everyone to make new friends, network, or even date, all over a table of good food and interesting conversation.

Fed up with having to meet people or date people via the usual online platforms and offline options, Janey and Remi created the ultimate dinner party website. Members choose their guests and accept or decline invitations. They can cater their dinner parties to whichever purpose they desire, be it business or social. The best part is there is no obligation to cook!

"One of our founder members hosted his dinner in an Eritrean restaurant, another bought in a fish and chip supper and another host cooked a three course meal - all worked brilliantly" says Janey.

Janey and Remi are building a vibrant hub of professional and outgoing people looking to meet other like minded people in a fun new way. Remi loves how their company has grown and the amazing people that have joined their community. "What's becoming clearer to us is that even though the guest list don't know each before dinner, the drive to create quality friendships, break bread together and use online to get offline, seems to be rousing a deep response and uniting our followers, which is really wonderful to see."

*photos by Milly Colley*

# SONGBIRD SESSIONS

GEMMA KNIGHT JONES, KELLY FRASER
& ALENA HEREL
MOB: 07904 733 090
@SESSIONSONGBIRD
BOOKSONGBIRDS@GMAIL.COM
SONGBIRDSESSIONS.COM

Singers Gemma Knight Jones, Kelly Fraser and Alena Herel came together to form an exquisite vocal trio, now known as Songbird Sessions. These soulful vocalists add a new dimension and atmosphere to corporate and private events, something a DJ could never achieve. "Whatever the occasion, we add a touch of sophistication and vivaciousness to your event."

Born out of friendship and an appreciation for one another's talents, the trio formed Songbird Sessions to fill a gap in the market. They wanted to do things differently - bring live music to unexpected locations and escape the confines of the music industry. By combining their vocal styles to appeal to a wide audience, the Songbird Sessions add something special to any event. "We add fun and fabulousness to every occasion. We promise to bring excellent vocals, energy and style to your event, making it the place to be!"

Each woman has her own successful career, but Songbird Sessions is a passion for them all. Although you can book them individually or as a duet, the trio ensemble is most popular. The three voices combined sing sweet harmonies and the group's visual style is unmistakable.

photos by Travel & Tone

# TRAVEL & TONE

THERESA AKWABOAH
@TRAVELANDTONE
INFO@TRAVELANDTONE.COM
TRAVELANDTONE.COM

Travel and Tone, as the name implies, offers fitness based holidays. These holidays are like no other - the luxury yoga retreats are held in beautiful, exclusive locations and the five star services are all provided by experts in their field. Founder Theresa Akwaboah and her team work towards the same goal - to help clients relax and recuperate.

"We provide the ideal break with the aim of helping busy people switch off from their day to day lives. We take a holistic approach to our clients' rest and relaxation. Our priority is to guide your body and mind to recover, feel revitalised and to find time for yourself."

A busy person herself, Theresa understands how valuable time is. Having attended a few disappointing retreats and holidays that left her more exhausted than when she arrived, she decided to create her own. Her retreats offer her clients the best of everything - daily yoga and other activities with leading instructors, renowned guest speakers (nutritionists, beauty experts, and many others), like minded company, delicious organic food, pampering massages, and beauty treatments.

Theresa works hard to exceed her client's expectations by paying close attention to the details and even providing an after care service. "Our core objective is to ensure people come away feeling they got what they needed out of their break and more besides."

# THE WOMEN'S WEALTH EXPERT

HANNAH FOXLEY
TEL: 020 7125 0409
@HANNAH_FOXLEY
INFO@THEWOMENSWEALTHEXPERT.CO.UK
THEWOMENSWEALTHEXPERT.CO.UK

Hannah Foxley is the Women's Wealth Expert and author of the Wealthy Divorcee. Specialising in financial planning for women, and in particular those dealing with divorce, she helps clients through the minefield of finance, leaving them feeling confident and secure.

A breast cancer survivor, Hannah decided she wanted to come at the financial industry with a fresh approach and put her own stamp on it. "Facing death when I had cancer is what encouraged and inspired me to start my business. I wanted to do something for myself and to make a difference to others."

Hannah's approach to finance comes from the heart; it's not just about the money, she is passionate about helping her clients achieve their goals. She recognises many women feel very vulnerable when it comes to financial planning, during divorce in particular. "I understand that this is a time when women are emotionally raw and really need guidance around the finances to help them to make objective financial decisions that will ensure long term security."

While completing a full financial plan for clients, Hannah begins by understanding, in depth, each client's goals and objectives for the future. By building strong relationships she is able to get to the core of what is really important to them. She provides recommendations to help them achieve their goals and after implementation monitors those solutions to keep them on track.

Ensuring women get the service they deserve,Hannah's fresh approach to finance and singular drive to succeed has paid off.

"Go for your dreams.
Many people will not get
your ideas or see what you can see.
Just remember sometimes the
opinions of others is just noise.
If you believe in your business,
you can make it happen!"

VANESSA VALLELY
*We Are The City*

# YUUGA KEMISTRI

ASA MARIA BJORNSDOTTIR
MOB: 07826 031 287
@YUUGAKEMISTRI
ASA@YUUGAKEMISTRI.COM
YUUGAKEMISTRI.WEEBLY.COM

*photos by Tom Parkinson*

Yuuga Kemistri teaches the benefits of a Raw Food diet through cooking classes, the Eating Raw for Real Beauty programme, and one-on-one consultations with founder Asa Maria Bjornsdottir. Helping people improve their body through what they eat and how they move, Asa also instructs regular Beauty yoga and Face Yoga classes.

Supporting customers who are ready to take their wellbeing into their own hands, Asa tells of her journey to good health and leads them into the world of Raw Food. "Food has always been my passion, and I'm in-love with life, art and healthy living. I'm dedicated to sharing my knowledge and experiences with others so that they may benefit in their own journey to good health, happiness, success, and longevity."

Teaching the masses in her cooking classes, students learn how to prepare simple yet delicious raw meals covering themes like Mexican, Asian and Guilt-free Cakes. The fresh ingredients whiz in blenders, squeeze through juicers and are chopped into delightfully flavourful meals. Nothing is cooked, and the meals are completely Vegan. The tasty meals surprise some, that a meal without heat or meat could be so filling, nourishing, and complete.

Satiating people's hunger to learn more about raw food diets, Asa is working on a number of recipe books. In the meantime, her one-on-one consultations and classes give clients the know-how to include raw food into their daily life. Whether the goal is to feel better, look better or both - Asa's tools and guidance satisfy their needs.

# ONLINE

Even though their online businesses are accessible everywhere, these entrepreneurs are still very much a part of London. Offering services coupled with London-based events or items designed in London-based studios, they are an important element of entrepreneurial London and a great reminder that electronic businesses still have real roots.

Accessible 24/7 through their delightful websites, they are a valuable source of information or wonderful items - these businesses offer it all at your fingertips. Although they are found, browsed and bought online, their services and products are best enjoyed while offline.

TheCity
Exclusive WATC Webinar
CLEO B
CLEO B

# CLEO B

CLEO BARBOUR
TEL: 020 3397 7082
@CLEO_BLONDON
INFO@CLEOB.COM
CLEOB.COM

CLEO B is a luxury footwear and accessory brand founded in 2009 by Cleo Barbour. Based in a funky studio, in Westbourne Park, CLEO B products are available online and in UK and International boutiques. Cleo's colourful designs are a favourite of celebrities like Jessie J and Paloma Faith and have received the attention of leading fashion magazines including Vogue, Grazia and InStyle.

Born into a family of entrepreneurs, Cleo was destined to start her own business, and as a teenager knew it was going to be in fashion. "After careful consideration I decided upon shoes as a starting point. They are challenging to design and make, but I love how they can give a woman instant confidence. They are, in my opinion, the most powerful item in your wardrobe."

Cleo's shoes give poise to women around the globe. The design's curvaceous shapes and rich suedes, patents, and snake skin materials make the shoes recognisably CLEO B. The shoes are feminine, wearable, comfortable, and fashionable. Many are also customisable by clipping on fur pom-poms, crystals or mini cassette tapes with Cleo's retro shoe clips.

A reflection of Cleo's style and her passion for colour, she is always setting trends. Her next step is a collection of colourful leather accessories and a wider range of shoe clips, giving even more options to her customers while always providing her collection of confidence-giving shoes.

*photos by Fanni Williams*

CLEO B

# KITTY DOLITTLE

ANDREA SEMAS
MOB: 07876 353 509
@KITTYDOLITTLE
CUSTOMERCARE@KITTYDOLITTLE.COM
KITTYDOLITTLE.COM

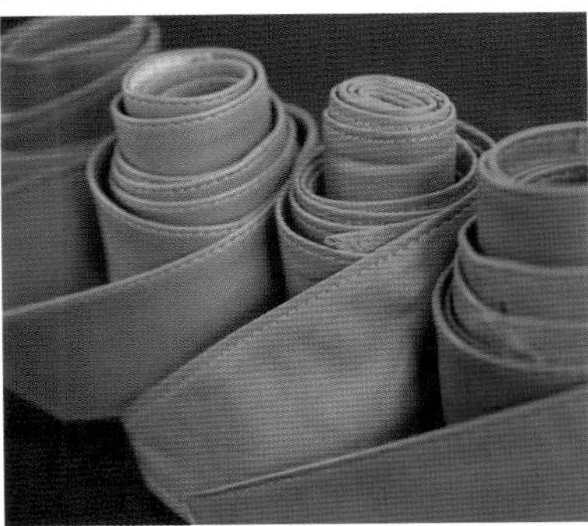

photos by Duncan Smith

Kitty DoLittle loves, and sells, luxury eco fashion accessories by passionate brands from around the world. Set up by Andrea Semas in 2010, the online company thrives on seeking out soulful, beautiful, and timeless pieces. With a focus on finding and promoting designers and labels that care about the resources they use for every aspect of their process, Kitty DoLittle makes "feel good fashion" accessible.

Having an eclectic upbringing, with a dad who designed and restored interiors for classic cars and airplanes, and a mom who had a love of collecting gemstones, jewellery, and vintage, it's unsurprising that Andrea developed a unique style preference. She favours and pursues 'slower', more sustainable fashion choices through her alter-ego Kitty DoLittle, a gregarious, confident, and thoughtful character. Her motto "DoLittle. Live a lot" is a reminder that by doing less, sometimes we can achieve more.

The online shop combines exceptional brands, passionate designers, and attainable price points. Amongst the eco-aware accessories are some exotic and intriguing top sellers, like the luxurious, much sought-after eel skin and lovely by-product leather handbags and clutches, in an array of styles and colours.

# SQUID LONDON

EMMA-JAYNE PARKES AND VIVIANE JAEGER
@SQUIDLONDON
HELLO@SQUIDLONDON.COM
SQUIDLONDON.COM

SquidLondon bring explosions of colour to the everyday with their unique line of umbrellas, rain capes and shower curtains. Co-founded at the London College of Fashion by Viviane Jaeger and Emma-Jayne Parkes, their signature Squidarellas, umbrellas with a brilliant, bold twist, become the ultimate walking piece of art in the always readily available London rain.

"We thought it would be so cool to walk down the street, it starts to rain and your clothes turn into a walking Jackson Pollock", say Viviane and Emma-Jayne. The pair took the idea and ran with it, sourcing a water-reactive ink and applying it to that epitome of a Londoner's accessory, the umbrella.

Both grew up with entrepreneurial parents so were prepared for the challenge of taking an idea from colourful concept to saleable product. Setting up their studio in East London, where they spent their University years, and thriving on the vibrant and colourful community, Viviane and Emma-Jayne create more than just another umbrella, rain cape or shower curtain.

"Our customers are interested in creativity regardless of whether they are creative or not. And most importantly they like to have FUN!", the pair say, and this sense of fun permeates through their business – their name, SquidLondon, whimsically references the cephalopod's ink-squirting trick.

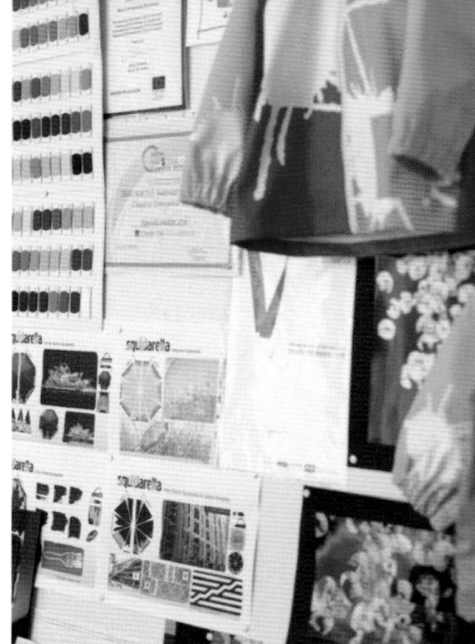

*photos by Milly Colley*

RODE

photos previous page top and this page by Fanni Williams; previous page bottom by Tree

# STITCHLESS TV

TREE
@STITCHLESS_TV
TREE@STITCHLESS.CO.UK
STITCHLESS.CO.UK

Prophesying the future, Tree had a vision of sewing becoming the new cooking. Doubted by TV production companies when she presented to them, Tree persevered and created Stitchless TV – an online channel teaching how to make clothes in minutes rather than days using Tree's stitchless speed sewing technique. Now presenting on BBC London radio and at workshops within John Lewis department stores, Tree is on a mission to teach people to sew, whether they are 6 or 86 years old.

"I want to be the Jamie Oliver of the sewing world, as I simplify the whole sewing experience, relying on good fabrics to do the talking thus making it accessible to all."

In addition to good fabrics, Tree created a method that simplifies sewing. She eliminated the need for pins or tacking making the process quicker, easier and, of course, much more pleasant. One of her most popular videos is "How to make a simple T-Shirt". By using an existing T-Shirt from your wardrobe, Tree helps the viewers make a unique one. The shirts have come to be known as 'Trophy T-Shirts' and show how simple sewing can be.

photos by Annie Armitage, portrait by John Cassidy

# WE ARE THE CITY

VANESSA VALLELY
TEL: 08453 402 704
@WATC_UPDATES
VANESSA.VALLELY@WEARETHECITY.COM
WEARETHECITY.COM

A valuable resource to women working in the UK, WeAreTheCity (WATC) is *the* website to visit. It provides recommendations and guidance across a wide range of female related topics, events and resources. Founded by Vanessa Vallely, born of her frustration while searching for information beneficial to female City-workers, she built the site with support from her husband. "I wanted to create a centralised hub to detail all of the different support groups and events that would help women to grow in their professional careers and personal lives."

Vanessa aggregates information from 120 women's networks and features over 250 expert writers on her site. With over 4 million hits per month, WATC is slowly becoming the little black book of resources for employed and entrepreneurial women.

Everything mentioned on the site has been specifically recommended or mandated by a WATC member. They also accept that they don't know all the answers, but will help point members and visitors in the right direction to lead them to the valuable answers they seek.

With the success of WATC, Vanessa took the next logical step and created Careers City (CareersCity.co.uk) connecting professional women in corporate roles with firms who are actively seeking to level the gender balance within their organisations.

Starting from an idea and a domain bought by her husband for twenty pounds, Vanessa has used her skills, determination and exuberant personality (she's a Pearly Queen) to help women in the City and across the UK make a greater impact, and to show "it's not just the boys that make the corporate world go round, it's the girls too!"

SPANX

wellicious
PRECIOUS WELLBEING

# WELLICIOUS

HEIKE SCHNELL
TEL: 020 7221 3300
@WELLICIOUS
INFO@WELLICIOUS.COM
WELLICIOUS.COM

*photos by Beatrix Fuhrmann*

Wellicious offers a range of stylish, eco-friendly yoga and Pilates clothing, loungewear, and wellbeing accessories produced in Europe. When founder Heike Schnell became a dedicated yogi, she searched for comfortable yet fashionable attire to fit her energetic lifestyle. Unable to find what she was looking for, she created Wellicious, bringing a sophisticated and fresh approach to yoga and Pilates clothing that is comfortable and feminine.

Careful attention is given to each piece; for example, the yoga pants - a top seller - have features that allow the wearer to focus on their yoga practice and not worry about adjusting their clothes. The Wellicious collection is so comfortable they can be worn anywhere and everywhere. Heike's customers, including celebrities like Gwyneth Paltrow, can be seen travelling, running errands or just lounging in her designs.

"Made from eco-friendly soft lyocell, our customers love them to practice both yoga and pilates in. They are even stylish enough to complete the school run in."

Living like a true yogi, Heike and her company give back by supporting the SOS Children's Village project in Peru with each member of staff sponsoring a different child. At home, Heike honours herself and her family knowing that, for entrepreneurs, there are many challenges. She recommends to others "never forget your family and ensure you can make a good balance between work and fun".

# INDUSTRY

The Industry section is the short-list to all the female entrepreneurs who are experts at helping other entrepreneurs. If you have been inspired to start your own business, or already have one, these are the women you need to know, the women that help build businesses and without whom we would not be successful: the coaches, graphic designers, accountants, and lawyers, the women we rely on to fill in our knowledge gaps.

Each has been specifically chosen for their skills and experience and can be trusted to help you on your journey through self-employment.

# B.HIVE

LYNNE FRANKS
TEL: 020 7717 8502
@BHIVECLUB
INFO@BHIVECLUB.COM
BHIVECLUB.COM

photos by B.Hive

Lynne Franks is a leader and advocate for women in business. As an author, entrepreneur and lifestyle guru, she has a communication reach that stretches across the world and is now giving women a place to be inspired and grow their businesses through her B.Hive business lounges.

"It has been my dream to create a new kind of business club where like-minded women can come together in a feminine space to network and share their stories."

Lynne has created B.Hive business lounges in London, Bristol and Manchester working in collaboration with Regus, the world's largest workspace provider. The stylish, feminine environments provide an ideal location to meet, network, or just escape the home office. Paired with practical, professional support through regular training sessions led by fellow B.Hive members, Lynne gives female entrepreneurs all the resources they need to succeed.

"It's clear that more women than ever are starting their own businesses, freelancing or taking leadership roles in large companies. But until now there just hasn't been anywhere to go where we can have meetings, catch up with our e-mails and hold events in a space that reflects 'the feminine way of doing business'."

## EXPERT ADVICE

WOMEN NEED THEIR OWN BEAUTIFUL SPACE TO CONNECT AND DO BUSINESS. FIND AN ENVIRONMENT THAT INSPIRES YOU - A PROFESSIONAL SPACE THAT REFLECTS YOUR PERSONAL VALUES AND TASTE.

# BRIGHT BLUE SKIES

LINDA WILLIAMS
@BRITEBLUESKIES
PROJECTS@BRIGHTBLUESKIES.COM
BRIGHTBLUESKIES.COM

## EXPERT ADVICE

BE CRYSTAL CLEAR HOW LONG YOU CAN SURVIVE ON SAVINGS BEFORE YOU HAVE TO MAKE ANY MONEY FROM YOUR NEW VENTURE.

Bright Blue Skies helps small and medium sized businesses achieve their goals, turning their vision into reality by working closely with owners and acting as a bite size general manager. Linda Williams understands where businesses want to go and helps make it happen - managing projects and ensuring progress is her forte. Linda makes sure that the things that need to happen, do.

After being told by one of the partners at the law firm where she worked to "stop talking about the kind of job you really want and just get on and do it", Linda took the encouragement, made the leap and started Bright Blue Skies.

Named after the feeling and energy a clear day brings, Bright Blue Skies becomes the "right-hand person" to small business owners. Searching for variety in her work, Linda took her love of business management and began working with small companies in sectors she found interesting. "I realised I didn't have to start the pickles company. I could work with the people who owned the pickle company, the art gallery, the café etc., and make their business lives simpler."

Taking on tasks big and small, Linda's clients rely on her, almost to the point of Linda becoming an extension of themselves. "Clients know I can do anything for them, and if I can't I will find someone who can. Even the smallest tasks are important, and I ensure they are completed to the highest quality."

Linda helps her clients fill the big picture with the small details and works diligently to make their dreams reality.

# CAVARA

LIZZIE PHILLIPS
36 SPITAL SQUARE, E1 6DY
TEL: 020 7375 7145
LIZZIE.PHILLIPS@CAVARA.NET
CAVARATRAINING.NET

## EXPERT ADVICE

THERE ARE SO MANY DIFFERENT MARKETING TOOLS WHICH CAN HELP YOU GET IN TOUCH WITH YOUR DREAM CLIENT. FOR EXAMPLE THE BEST TIME TO SEND AN EMAIL CAMPAIGN IS 11AM ON A TUESDAY AND TRY AND USE A P.S IN YOUR DIRECT MAIL LETTER FOR A BETTER RESPONSE RATE.

Cavara is a one-stop shop for business support services from bookkeeping to marketing. Led by Lizzie Phillips, Cavara also provides entrepreneurs with the skills they need to effectively run their businesses through one-to-one tutorials and interactive marketing workshops.

A marketing and PR consultant, Lizzie has experience helping many companies and organisations. Although she and Cavara can do the work, Lizzie prefers teaching entrepreneurs how to do it themselves. Her most popular course is 'Marketing in a Nutshell' - a one day course covering all the different marketing techniques such as social media, email marketing, and direct mail. At the end delegates leave feeling inspired and able to create their own winning marketing campaign.

"I give entrepreneurs the tools to do it themselves, giving them the flexibility to create a campaign that is right for their own business, and gives them the best ROI!"

Always looking for ways to share her expertise, Lizzie has written a book detailing her trade tips entitled 'Lizzie Phillips' Marvellous Marketing Manual'. She is also available for one-to-one three-hour tutorials where a client can bring their own existing marketing materials and leave with a brand new marketing plan.

Having received testimonials from everyone she has worked with, Lizzie's lessons and advice have clearly made an impressive impact on many.

# ESTHER STANHOPE, THE PRESENTER COACH

ESTHER STANHOPE
MOB: 07780 994 478
@ESTHERSTANHOPE1
ESTHER@ESTHERSTANHOPE.COM
ESTHERSTANHOPE.COM

## EXPERT ADVICE

IT'S NOT ABOUT 'ME' WHEN PRESENTING IT'S ABOUT 'YOU'. YOU WOULDN'T BE PRESENTING IF YOU DIDN'T HAVE AN AUDIENCE, AND THEY BRING AS MUCH TO THE PARTY AS YOU. ENGAGE WITH YOUR AUDIENCE, LOOK AT THEM, INCLUDE THEM, ASK THEM QUESTIONS, REFER TO THEM, MAKE THEM SMILE, MAKE THEM THINK, PLAY THE ROOM. IT MAKES FOR A MUCH MORE POWERFUL PRESENTATION.

Esther Stanhope, The Presenter Coach, provides Personal Impact and Presentation Skills Training for professionals who need to look and sound good in front of an audience. Be it on television, radio, or in a boardroom, the training is designed to give people confidence when speaking in public.

Esther coaches her clients using her own practical, creative and fun techniques inspired by her background in television and radio. "Having worked with the good, the great and the difficult for 20 years, I know what makes people tick."

Encouraged by friends to make the most of her ability to read people, she decided to start her own business not only coaching performers in the entertainment industry, but professionals and corporate businessmen/women in the City.

Esther helps her clients become the best version of themselves. She films all her coaching sessions and sends edited highlights and detailed feedback about their body language, vocal qualities and confidence levels, and continues to work with them in order for them to reach their potential.

Allowing her clients to show vulnerability without judgement, Esther develops meaningful relationships - one where constructive criticism is well received and not taken personally. Clients gain confidence from completing the training and are ready to speak in any situation.

# FUSE ACCOUNTANTS LLP

FAYE WATTS
TEL: 020 8342 7390
@FUSEACCOUNTANTS
INFO@FUSEACCOUNTANTS.CO.UK
FUSEACCOUNTANTS.CO.UK

## EXPERT ADVICE

KEEP THE BOOKKEEPING/RECORDKEEPING UP TO DATE. UNDERSTAND THE BASIC PRINCIPALS OF TAX PLANNING AND ALWAYS TAKE ADVICE.

FUSE Accountants are an independent firm of Chartered Certified Accountants, business advisors, and tax specialists. Founded by Faye Watts in 2008, the firm provides efficient business and tax planning to established and growing businesses, specialising in entertainment, fashion, media, and property. Faye effectively avoids corporate stereotypes and works hard to make tax less scary.

Providing full accountancy services, Faye and her team make complex advice seem straight forward. They work closely with their clients through a hands-on approach and help them better understand their business's financial needs. Keeping in touch throughout the year, rather than just at tax time, Faye helps her clients manage their on-going business.

"FUSE is about working together and joining forces with our clients, combining our expertise and knowledge within the practice to help clients. On a lighter note, we like to give a FUn and SErious approach."

Staying true to her profession, Faye recommends to fellow and aspiring entrepreneurs "Follow your dreams but make sure the numbers really do work and be realistic!"

# GLOBAL INSTITUTE FOR EXTRAORDINARY WOMEN

BEA BENKOVA
@THEGIFEW
INFO@GIFEW.ORG
GIFEW.ORG

Founded by Bea Benkova, the Global Institute for Extraordinary Women is a holistic and spiritual way of not just looking at life, but at how we do business. They provide transformational education programs for women who want to make a difference in their own lives and the lives of others around them.

After learning her mother had cancer, Bea had a defining moment in her life. "My mother's response to the news staggered me and will always stay vivid in my memory. 'Why now, when I've finally let go and have time to live my life?' she said to the doctor. Why now? A successful woman, my mother had focused almost exclusively on business and family; no time to stop and really think about what she loved doing." Feeling that her future was on the same path, Bea left her career in the City and began a journey of personal transformation, which led her to redefining her purpose and living a fulfilled life while making a difference.

Since Bea left banking in early 2007, she has inspired, empowered and guided prominent women around the world, including leading executives, entrepreneurs, politicians and artists. "I help them discover and express their unique talent, femininity, and leadership so that they can naturally fulfil their potential and purpose, experience vitality and fulfilment, sustainably increase their performance at work, and be a valuable contribution to the organisations and communities they belong to."

## EXPERT ADVICE

FIND OTHER PEOPLE AND ENTREPRENEURS WHO ARE DOING WHAT YOU ARE DOING, CONNECT WITH THEM AND START TO CREATE COLLABORATIONS AND SYNERGIES. DO NOT DO IT ON YOUR OWN. YOU WILL BE NICELY SURPRISED THAT THE IMPACT YOU CREATE IS MUCH BIGGER.

# KAREN HALLER COLOUR & DESIGN

KAREN HALLER
TEL: 020 7727 4938
@KARENHALLER
HELLO@KARENHALLER.CO.UK
KARENHALLER.CO.UK

## EXPERT ADVICE

YOUR BUSINESS BRAND IS NOT ABOUT YOU. THE BEST COLOURS FOR YOUR BUSINESS TO WEAR MAY BE THE TOTAL OPPOSITE OF WHAT YOU WOULD CONSIDER WEARING YOURSELF. THE BEST FAVOUR YOU COULD DO FOR YOUR BUSINESS IS GIVE IT ITS OWN PERSONALITY THAT ALIGNS WITH THE SERVICE YOU ARE OFFERING. AND THAT'S WHAT SELLS.

Karen Haller is one of the leading authorities in the field of applied colour psychology, helping businesswomen worldwide create remarkable brand personalities. Because people react to colour before words or shapes, colour is the missing link to making the emotional connection with clients. Colour is in fact a silent sales force. Karen's online products, workshops and private consultations help attract your ideal clients. By going beyond and applying the physics and psychology of colour to your brand, you gain a unique competitive edge.

While working a day-job in IT and studying design at night, Karen felt her future was in combining her creative and analytical skills. She discovered this perfect combination in the science of applied colour psychology. "I began to realise the power of colour and wanted to understand it at a much deeper level; a psychological level."

After studying extensively with leading colour experts and psychologists in Australia and the UK, Karen developed unique ways of applying colour psychology to business branding, business interiors and business clothing.

Her forte is helping businesses maximise the impact of their brand resulting in stronger brand recognition, loyalty and increased profits. This kind of impact can only be created through truly understanding the science behind colour. It's a process that goes far beyond just mere decoration or design.

HIGHLIGHT
INDUSTRY
MONICA
VINADER

"I always new I wanted to start my own business, from a young age, but it was my Father that kept encouraging me, he was a business owner himself and often used to say… 'so when are you going it alone?' So I did…."

CHERYL LAIDLAW OWNER OF REYL DESIGNS

"My friends who were in full time work and not following their dreams encouraged me to take the leap and following my passion, my heart. Being in business it is really important to have a close network of friends, confidantes to inspire and encourage you."

KAREN HALLER COLOUR & DESIGN

Inspiration to begin a business comes from many places or people. It can be a comment someone makes, a desire or need for something unavailable, or encouragement from a friend that leads you to the ideal business idea - the lightbulb moment.

For many of the entrepreneurs, the person who encouraged them has continued to support them in following their dreams and passions to build the outstanding businesses they have today.

# LUSCINIA CONSULTING

NADIA MARTINE KOCH
MOB: 07837 947 459
@LUSCINIACONSULT
NADIA@LUSCINIA-CONSULTING.COM
LUSCINIA-CONSULTING.COM

## EXPERT ADVICE

AN AUDIENCE, WHETHER AT A SEMINAR, A BOARD ROOM OR AT A SALES MEETING, MIMIC THE SPEAKER. SO TO ACTIVELY ENGAGE THEM TO LISTEN, MAKE SURE YOU PHYSICALLY LISTEN WHEN YOU TALK. TILT YOUR HEAD SLIGHTLY SHOWING ONE EAR, NOD WHEN YOU MAKE IMPORTANT POINTS AND GESTURE IN FRONT OF YOUR BODY TO CREATE AN ENERGY FLOW. AND NOTICE HOW YOUR AUDIENCE SIT UP AND PAY ATTENTION!

Luscinia Consulting has its roots in the artistic world but is aimed at the corporate market, offering training in non-verbal communication, public speaking and media. Through a variety of workshops and one-to-one sessions, founder Nadia Koch helps build her clients confidence and stamina, giving them the tools they need to make sure they engage with their audience when making a pitch or giving presentations.

With years of experience as an actress and working in the business world, Nadia recognised a recurring issue, "a lot of people - and women in particular - fail to reach their full potential and succeed within their business because they cannot confidently communicate their passion and sell their ideas".

Seeking to address this problem, Nadia developed courses to teach clients how to perfect body language when speaking to small or large groups, find their confidence and never blank, stumble or undersell themselves again.

"The passion my clients have for their businesses is truly inspirational, and that is why it is important for me to make sure they succeed."

Nadia's clients are dedicated to their businesses and inspire her as they work together to reveal their full potential and make sure they "sing" with a true voice, relaxed and free. Nadia named her business Luscinia, the Latin word for nightingale, in reference to the voice she inspires in her clients and a favourite fairytale, "The Nightingale", by fellow Dane, Hans Christian Andersen.

# MAHON DIGITAL

SAIJA MAHON
TEL: 01920 444 399
@MAHONDIGITAL
SAIJA@MAHONDIGITAL.CO.UK
MAHONDIGITAL.CO.UK

## EXPERT ADVICE

GOOGLE IS SO POWERFUL NOWADAYS, IF YOUR WEBSITE AND PRODUCTS ARE NOT VISIBLE ON GOOGLE, YOUR BUSINESS MAY AS WELL NOT EXIST. IT'S DRAMATIC, BUT SO TRUE.

Mahon Digital, founded by Saija Mahon, help promote and grow businesses through planning, creating, managing, and executing complex and effective online marketing strategies. With locations in the UK and Scandinavia, they bring international experience, expertise, and know-how of several markets to their clients.

Hailing from a family of entrepreneurs, Saija had the confidence to turn her interest in marketing and advertising into a successful company just months after her daughter was born. "I always wanted to have my own business one day. I was inspired and encouraged by my family when starting my business and now my dream has come true."

Saija modestly credits the success of her business to her "wonderful team". Rather than merely operating as an external marketing support agency, Saija and her team strives to collaborate with each client, going the extra mile to understand their core business and business objectives.

Bringing online success to businesses ranging in size and spanning a variety of industries including retail, technology, and the professional services, Mahon Digital is a valuable addition to any businesses marketing strategy.

# THE NON EXEC HUB

HEATHER WHITE
MOB: 07775 855 764
@NONEXECHUB
HEATHER@NONEXECHUB.COM
NONEXECHUB.COM

## EXPERT ADVICE

THIS IS A JOURNEY AND YOU WILL NEED A NETWORK EVERY STEP OF THE WAY. EVERY STAGE OF YOUR JOURNEY YOUR NETWORK NEEDS TO EVOLVE WITH YOU. SO KEEP MEETING PEOPLE AND DEVELOPING THESE RELATIONSHIPS. NEVER STOP THINKING WHO NEXT DO YOU NEED TO MEET, THINK 12 MONTHS IN THE FUTURE AND PLAN TO MEET THEM.

When Heather White attended a launch for a Non-Executive Directors (NED) and Trustees network, her only thought was "oh no, another one?!" Realising there were many different people all trying to accomplish the same thing, Heather set about consolidating the community by creating The Non Exec Hub, a UK based independent online directory and community for people who are, or aspire to be, Non Executive Directors, Chairs or Trustees.

Heather included on her website the majority of NED/Trustee membership groups, Executive Search agencies, training services, and related free information sources. She even has the support of a team of Executive Coaches who can help anyone seeking to advance their careers in this rewarding field.

Through membership, individuals have access to all they need to know about becoming a NED or Trustee. Heather realised the people who volunteer for these roles are busy but want to give back. From a survey, she discovered "their primary reason for taking on these roles is all about contribution. Something has affected their lives to drive that level of commitment and energy."

Using her skills and experience from her other successful company, Smarter Networking, Heather has already simplified this over-complicated area. And with advice from one of her mentors, Vanessa Vallely (page 196), she knows that with passion, insight, determination, and energy she will be able to overcome any new barrier and create the hub that NED's and Trustees require.

# OFF TO SEE MY LAWYER

JOANNA TALL
TEL: 020 8946 2355
INFO@OFFTOSEEMYLAWYER.COM
OFFTOSEEMYLAWYER.COM

## EXPERT ADVICE

REMEMBER THAT WEBSITES NEED TO BE LEGAL TOO. MANY WEBSITE DEVELOPERS DO NOT REALISE THIS AND HAND OVER YOUR WEBSITES TO YOU WITH NO TERMS AT ALL AND YOU COULD BE BREAKING THE LAW FROM THE MOMENT YOU GO LIVE. ALWAYS CONSULT A LAWYER AT THE OUTSET RATHER THAN WHEN THINGS GO WRONG; IT WILL ACTUALLY BE CHEAPER!

Off to see my Lawyer specialises in advising female entrepreneurs with businesses in the UK. Founded by Jo Tall, her mission is to provide legal advice that is clear and affordable and to take the fear out of consulting a lawyer. She has even created an on-line 'oven ready' document shop, selling legal templates specifically for start -ups.

After attending a Leadership for Women course, Jo took the leap to start her own business. She recognised the gap in the market; there were no lawyers specialising in advising female entrepreneurs, none that would make them comfortable, that understood the hours they kept, and none that could speak their language. Jo set out to become that lawyer.

"I offer legal advice in a non-scary way, I am told. My clients feel they can call any time, and there will not be a sense of a clock ticking. My team are also working mums and work around their families; they understand the need to be flexible."

Wanting to convey that feeling of comfort and casualness in her company name, Jo chose "Off to see my Lawyer" and she is now also known as 'legal Mary Poppins' - a reputation that is far from the typical, stuffy lawyer many imagine.

Offering an abundance of free resources and the opportunity to join a community of other clients to share experiences, working with Jo provides much more than just legal advice!

# PITCH PERFECT CLUB

EMMA STROUD
TEL: 01928 503 777
@PITCHPERFECTUK
EMMA@PITCHPERFECTCLUB.COM
PITCHPERFECTCLUB.COM

## EXPERT ADVICE

WHEN DOING A TALK, PRESENTATION OR PITCH, SPEND AS MUCH PRACTICING YOUR DELIVERY OUT LOUD AS PERFECTING THE CONTENT. YOU COULD HAVE THE MOST CAPTIVATING SPEECH WRITTEN BUT IF YOU END UP FAILING TO CONNECT WITH YOUR AUDIENCE, YOUR MESSAGE WILL BE POWERLESS. BE AWARE OF YOUR VOICE, EYE CONTACT AND HOW YOU CAN MAKE USE OF BODY LANGUAGE TO OPTIMISE YOUR PRESENCE.

Pitch Perfect Club makes it easier to master public speaking. Created by Emma Stroud and Deon Newbronner, the club gives members an opportunity to build confidence when speaking, presenting and pitching through a variety of events and one-on-one coaching.

Emma wanted to provide a community for successful business owners to connect and better themselves – people who were looking to take the next step. "Our twenty years of experience helping business owners present and pitch better repeatedly showed us the value of building personal presence for business success. We believe that our unique club model facilitates this and gives clients the support they need to make that success a reality."

Building on Emma and Deon's experience as theatre professionals and executive coaches, they have created a programme that gives members all the tools they need to take their profile and their business to the next level. Throughout the year, members have the opportunity to speak in front of an audience and meet and learn from one another at the Club's exclusive events. They also receive six hour-long sessions of one-to-one development and four half-day peer learning sessions.

Always practising her own public speaking skills, Emma moonlights as a comedy performer, doing improvisation both solo and as part of a national group. "It certainly keeps me on my toes!"

“Follow your dreams,
but do it with the support of
a partner, as it is very hard to
work on your own when
running a business.”

ROSALIND RATHOUSE
*Cookery School*

# THE PIXEL PUSHER LTD

ANNA COWIE
MOB: 07814 927 936
ANNA@THEPIXELPUSHER.CO.UK
THEPIXELPUSHER.CO.UK

## EXPERT ADVICE

GET INVOLVED. START BRAVE AND BRASH: YOU CAN ALWAYS MAKE THINGS MORE CONSERVATIVE, BUT IT'S HARD TO MAKE THINGS MORE RADICAL. EMPATHIZE. RISK EVERYTHING. NETWORK. SIMPLIFY. BE AUTHENTIC AND INSPIRING EVERYDAY.

Founded in 2004 by Anna Cowie and her partner Spencer Kebbell, The Pixel Pusher Ltd is an innovative graphic design and branding agency. 'Bringing your brand to life in a multi-channel world' The Pixel Pusher team have worked tangentially with a diverse range of companies to successfully launch new brands, and develop existing brands.

Dedicated to "saving the world from bad design, one pixel at a time", Anna and her team will become part of a client's team, offering both in-house and outsource solutions for their complete design and branding needs. Imagination and innovation are two driving forces for The Pixel Pusher team - whether it be a social media 'tweet' or a campaign message on an outdoor billboard, they believe 'brandedness' is the foundation for all that follows.

"We work with customers that are driven to succeed and are looking to create unique brands and understand the value branding can have on a business's growth. Clients come to us not only for our graphic design services, but also for our ability to collaborate and become an integral partner to their business growth and evolution on a day-to-day basis." Armed with a design blueprint at the end of the project, the Pixel Pusher can then help the client to continually evolve their branding and design.

With an entrepreneurial spirit and ability to think outside the box, Anna ensures her client's companies are represented at their best through their branding; continuing to evolve both creatively and competitively.

# REDEFINING LIFE

TERESA MITROVIC
TEL: 020 7193 5545
@TERESAMITROVIC
INFO@REDEFININGLIFECOACHING.COM
REDEFININGLIFECOACHING.COM

## EXPERT ADVICE

RECONNECT DAILY TO WHAT'S WORKING, WHAT'S NOT, WHAT YOU'VE LEARNED, AND WHAT MATTERS MOST TO YOU. THE LEARNING CURVE MIGHT SURPRISE YOU, SO BE PATIENT AND STAY OPEN TO LEARNING AND REMEMBER THAT FAILURE IS SIMPLY PART OF HONING YOUR SUCCESS.

After a single day of coaching training over a decade ago, Teresa Mitrovic had a realisation that career success and family life could go hand in hand. The results were outstanding, "My work was easier, and rather than feeling overwhelmed and exhausted, I was energised and inspired which had profound results in my life professionally and personally. I knew then that I wanted to help others to find the same freedom and success in their careers."

Now coaching executives and entrepreneurs, she leads people to well-balanced lives with satisfying and sustainable careers. She helps clients redefine what success means for them and what will give them the greatest career satisfaction helping them achieve a work life balance. "Redefining Life is about taking a breath, pausing to consider what matters and then realigning your career to create a life much less ordinary and much more fulfilling."

Through her Bespoke Programme, Teresa tailors the timing, structure, and content of engagement to suit each client's working style and ambitions. She blends a variety of disciplines including NLP, traditional coaching, somatic coaching, positive psychology, neuroscience, and mindfulness to achieve exceptional success with her clients.

"I have a unique style - part fan, part cheerleader, part taskmaster, and I'm authentic - I live by the principles I teach."

Teresa coaches passionate, dedicated, and ambitious people whose greatest strength (putting others above themselves), has often become their greatest weakness. She guides them to a redefined, balanced life while enabling career longevity and personal success.

# REYL DESIGN GROUP

CHERYL LAIDLAW
MOB: 07866 683 436
@CHERYL_LAIDLAW
CHERYL@REYL.CO.UK
REYL.CO.UK

## EXPERT ADVICE

DESIGN LOGOS, WEBSITES AND PRINT MATERIAL WITH THE END USER ALWAYS IN MIND. YOU HAVE 4 SECONDS TO MAKE A LASTING IMPRESSION. MAKE SURE IT'S A GOOD ONE.

Cheryl Laidlaw has had a love affair with design for as long as she can remember and her desire to have her own business was positively encouraged by her Father. The name 'Reyl' is a combination of Real and Cheryl - it sums up her ideals, values, and beliefs about the role design plays in creating brands that have stand out appeal and make an outstanding impression.

"My role is to get to the very core of a client's business, understand the essence of their brand and find out what makes their business special. It's a process that produces a creative solution that is both beautiful and business savvy. I will always be honest, often challenging, and always mindful of making their budget an investment that pays dividends."

Cheryl offers a tempting menu of design packages. The most popular is the full business design service, including logo creation, high impact websites, business cards that bring business, and social media set-up so clients can implement initiatives that lead to brand engagement, increased awareness, and a buzz about their business.

"I take my clients on a journey. Often emotional. Extremely personal. When we reach the destination it's always a eureka moment. There's no better feeling than seeing a delighted client."

Cheryl is an avid networker. The bulk of her business comes from referrals. Her recommendation to aspiring entrepreneurs is to make meaningful connections with other business owners. "Join an established organisation. Dip into ad-hoc events, or throw yourself into the world of social media. It's not just about who you know, it's about who knows you."

# SELLING FROM THE HEART

CATHERINE WATKIN
TEL: 033 3240 9965
@CATHWATKIN
INFO@CATHERINEWATKIN.COM
SELLINGFROMTHEHEART.COM

EXPERT ADVICE

ALWAYS ASK "PERMISSION" TO SELL. RATHER THAN LAUNCHING IN WITH HOW WONDERFUL YOUR BUSINESS OR PRODUCT IS, SAY "FROM WHAT YOU'VE TOLD ME, I REALLY THINK THAT MY SERVICE WILL HELP YOU. IS IT OK IF I TELL YOU A LITTLE MORE ABOUT IT AND HOW IT WOULD WORK?" IF THEY SAY "YES" INSTEAD OF A CLIENT "BACKING AWAY", YOU HAVE AN ENGAGED CLIENT OPEN TO LISTENING AND READY TO MAKE A DECISION THAT'S RIGHT FOR THEM.

Selling from the Heart, founded by Catherine Watkin, helps female business owners sell their services and products in a non-pushy way that feels authentic and comfortable for both the seller and the client.

After training as a coach and NLP Practitioner, Catherine noticed she was excelling at getting new clients when her colleagues were struggling. "I realised that my 17 years sales experience - rather than something I was trying to escape from to find something more meaningful - was in fact my Gift, and the vehicle for me to make a real difference to the lives of other women through helping their businesses to succeed."

Catherine works with heart-centred business owners - people who are in business to pursue a passion or make a difference - who know that if they are to be successful they need to be able to sell, but feel uncomfortable with traditional sales methods. She teaches them her non-pushy, yet practical and effective sales techniques. A majority of her clients take the 8 week online programme, "Get More Clients Saying 'Yes!'". The training is so effective that most people recoup their investment from increased sales by the end of the course. Catherine also shares her knowledge via regular live workshops and training, one-to-one consulting, and private business mentoring.

Catherine, a heart-centred business owner herself, believes "If we come to our businesses as our true authentic selves then the business becomes an extension of our personality and values, and that is incredibly rewarding". Always working with integrity and authenticity, Catherine helps others have success in their business without compromising their values.

photos: by Annie Armitage; except next page bottom left by Lucy Williams

# SISTER SNOG

ANNIE BROOKS & HELA WOZNIAK-KAY
TEL: 020 8852 0101
@SISTERSNOG
CONNECT@SISTERSNOG.COM
SISTERSNOG.COM

Annie Brooks and Hela Wozniak-Kay are the heart and soul of Sister Snog. Together they have put their individual hallmark on the London networking landscape by creating a brand full of sizzle and a business full of buzz - a remarkable club for successful business women.

They became avid networkers while running their boutique branding consultancy - Snog The Agency. Although referrals led to a range of colourful clients, something was missing. The networking scene in London at that time lacked sparkle, style and a sense of belonging. So, on the first Friday of February 2002, Annie and Hela hosted their first ever business event "An intimate lunch. Two clients. Two prospects. On the menu? Business with a capital 'B'."

Today Sister Snog is a catalyst that brings go-getting women together, both in the social media world and face-to-face at a calendar of sparkling events. Every event is a mini marketing platform. "A fabulous opportunity for members to meet in distinctive venues and open doors for each other, taking them one step closer to their next big win, dream client or raving fan."

Membership is selective and by invitation only. Members are handpicked. The Directors meet each and every prospective member in person to ensure there's a perfect fit, based on chemistry and intuition, as well as the very best business credentials. "Members are decision makers. They're brand savvy, well connected, have fallen in love with social media and see the benefit of 'making-friends-&-finding-fans' to help catapult their business to heady heights."

## EXPERT ADVICE

GET CONNECTED. JOIN A TRIBE. FIND A MENTOR. WATCH THE TEDTALKS. READ VORACIOUSLY. FOLLOW YOUR INTUITION. SHARE YOUR KNOWLEDGE. GET PAID FOR YOUR EXPERTISE. BECOME A SOCIAL BUTTERFLY. FIND A NICHE AND OWN IT. NEVER SAY PLEASE. ALWAYS SAY THANK YOU.

"Fail as fast as you can.
Dust yourself off,
and then do it again.
But improve it!"

ANDREA SEMAS
*Kitty DoLittle*

# SOFIE SANDELL DIGITAL LEADERSHIP & CREATIVITY

SOFIE SANDELL
@SOFFI_PROPP
HELLO@SOFIESANDELL.COM
SOFIESANDELL.COM

## EXPERT ADVICE

MANY PEOPLE FEEL A BIT STUCK WHEN IT COMES TO THE DIGITAL WORLD. THERE IS PLENTY OF INFORMATION OUT THERE, JUST GOOGLE IT. THE CHALLENGE IS TO PUT ALL THE INFORMATION INTO CONTEXT AND MAKE IT WORK FOR YOU AND YOUR BUSINESS.

Sofie Sandell coaches her clients on how to make the most of digital and social media using digital leadership and creativity principles. She helps clients put digital opportunities into context.

Sofie feels digital leadership is about being a creative leader. During her various workshops, she coaches people and helps them open their eyes to what's possible using digital tools. "Digital and social media can be scary and you need to switch on your creative mind to be open for change and new digital opportunities."

Working directly with CEOs, Managing Directors, or founders, Sofie finds it a privilege to learn about their businesses and challenges. She loves teaching and coaching people about how the digital world works, and wants to share her knowledge with more people. This drive inspired her to write her book 'Digital Leadership', which teaches people how to use creativity better and how to grab the digital opportunities available.

# WINNING IMPRESSION

KATRINA COLLIER
MOB: 07917 880 711
@WINNINGIMPRESS
INFO@WINNINGIMPRESSION.COM
WINNINGIMPRESSION.COM

## EXPERT ADVICE

EMBRACE SOCIAL MEDIA AS A MEANS TO PROMOTE YOURSELF AND DEFINITELY EMBRACE GOOGLE+, YES I SAID GOOGLE+. KEEP YOUR PROFILES' KEYWORDS RICH SO YOU CAN BE FOUND AND TAILOR THEM TO THE DIFFERENT AUDIENCE, USE A PROFESSIONAL PROFILE PICTURE, AND SUCCEED BY SHARING GREAT CONTENT, TIPS, AND ADVICE.

Social Media is intertwined into every part of our life and is now taking over the recruitment industry. Winning Impression's founder Katrina Collier trains others and speaks about the successful use of social media for recruitment. She shows companies how to recruit the best people directly through social media, effectively saving them time and money. Katrina also empowers job seekers with the knowledge to open employment opportunities through effective social networking.

After realising that companies and job seekers were struggling to navigate through social media in order to find employees and employment, Katrina decided to step in. "I saw that there was little help around for companies who want to use social media to recruit the best people, whilst saving time, money, and frustration, or for job seekers who want to use it to open hidden job opportunities by gaining access to companies directly."

Katrina trains hiring companies through her 'Social Media for Recruitment' workshops. The courses teach techniques to efficiently look for and contact people on multiple social media sites, giving them control of their recruitment and, in particular, of the quality of the hire and the associated costs.

Determined to demystify the use of social media for recruitment and job searching, Katrina's passion is infectious. She brings clarity to an otherwise overwhelming experience.

# YOUR LOCAL PR

AMANDA RUIZ
TEL: 01206 240 220
MOB: 07711 419 595
@YOURLOCALPR
HELLO@YOURLOCALPR.CO.UK
YOURLOCALPR.CO.UK

## EXPERT ADVICE

DO LOTS OF RESEARCH ABOUT YOUR CLIENT AND WHO YOUR CLIENT WOULD LIKE TO BE INTRODUCED TO, THEN CHARM THE GATEKEEPER!

YourLocalPR are experts at connecting people with key contacts through PR and marketing strategies. Founder Amanda Ruiz helps her clients acquire new customers and raise their profile and brand awareness.

The daughter of an entrepreneur, Amanda learned from a young age the hard working ethic needed to run a successful business. After starting her own luxury brand e-commerce store, Amanda realised her passion was helping other business owners attract more clients and increase sales.

Amanda helps entrepreneurs, similar to her, with vision and ambition. She uses her marketing and PR skills, extensive contacts, tenacity, go-getter spirit, and expertise to help her clients. "They don't have the time to shout from the rooftops about themselves, so I do that for them. I will roll my sleeves up and work incredibly hard to get the results my clients deserve."

Admitting entrepreneurship is hard work, with long hours and a few set backs, she encourages others to just go for it. "Running your own business requires passion and enthusiasm - if you have those two qualities, follow your dream. However, if the first path you take isn't the one you started on, you can evolve your business using your acquired skills and move onwards and upwards!"

# PHOTOGRAPHERS

## ANNIE ARMITAGE

ANNIEARMITAGE.COM

Annie is one of the UK's leading family lifestyle photographers and based in South West London. As an "on location" photographer her family work produces a wide range of images covering pregnancy, newborns, babies, under five's, older children, and teenagers. Her main aim is to capture families enjoying moments together and create memories through her photography which will be passed from generation to generation.

## SERENA BOLTON

SERENABOLTON.COM

Serena is a photographer living in London. Her passion for photography was sparked whilst travelling in India at eighteen and she has been a keen traveller and photographer from that moment on. Since becoming a mother to two boys, Serena has rarely put her camera down and over the years she has evolved and grown her portfolio from family portraiture to more commercial work with major brands Hermes.

## MILLY COLLEY

MILLYCOLLEY.COM

Milly is a London-based photographer inspired by fashion, fine art, and femininity. Her work has been featured in many print and online publications including The Mail on Sunday, Photography Monthly and Professional Photographer magazines. Clients include Topshop, Urban Outfitters, Gucci Group and American Airlines. She works with digital and an assortment of film cameras, her favourite being a beloved 62-year-old Leica IIIf.

## CHARLOTTE FIELDING

CHARLOTTEFIELDINGPHOTOGRAPHY.COM

Charlotte Fielding is a London based professional photographer who works throughout the UK, Europe, and the USA. Educated at Nottingham University with an MA from Sothebys International, Charlotte specialises in carefully observed travel, event, product, and portraiture imagery. She is accredited at Tate Museums, Kew Gardens, and The Museum of London and works on a regular basis with the Spanish Tourist Office and The Princes Trust.

## BEATRIX FUHRMANN

BEATRIXFUHRMANNPHOTOGRAPHY.CO.UK

Beatrix is a photographer with a focus on wedding & family photography. She has a background in media technology and is a people person who loves to capture expressions, emotions and details - telling stories with her photography. She is also interested in photographing small businesses and portraits. She lives with her family in North London, Muswell Hill.

## RASHMI GILL

VIVIDCLICKS.COM

Being a family lawyer didn't help to quench Rashmi's artistic hunger. Ever since childhood, Rashmi was always photographing every precious moment. Today, she is an international photographer known for her commercial and family photography and renowned for her ability to capture genuine, tender family moments. She is particularly sought after by families with young children who want ever lasting memories.

## FANNI WILLIAMS

SUPERFLY-CREATIVE.COM

Superfly Creative Ltd is a London based graphic design and lifestyle photography company established in 2007 by Fanni Williams. With over ten years in the design industry, Superfly Creative can help you create an awesome looking brand for your business, both online and in print. In addition, Fanni's fresh, editorial style of photography is perfect for eye-catching fashion look-books and stylish product photography.

## LUCY WILLIAMS

MYHEARTSKIPPED.CO.UK

Lucy Williams is a wedding, portrait and women's photographer shooting vibrant, playful, natural light imagery. She often photographs people in love and more often photographs people in love with life itself. She is renowned for making people feel confident and comfortable in front of the lens, an eye for detail and a talent for capturing the atmosphere of any celebration.

# CONTRIBUTORS

## ANNA COWIE - ART AND DESIGN DIRECTION

The Pixel Pusher is a graphic design and branding agency which develops strategies, creative campaigns and design collateral for their clients.They are skilled in producing well-crafted brand identities from conception, through to the practicalities of packaging and print and web designs.They understand what it takes to make a brand heard, by conveying the client's message to an audience as memorably as possible.

## KAREN HALLER - COLOUR AND DESIGN EXPERT

Karen Haller is one of the leading authorities in the field of applied colour psychology, helping businesswomen worldwide create remarkable brand personalities. People react to colour before words or shapes meaning it is the missing link to truly make the emotional connection to your clients. It is in fact your silent sales force.Through her online products, workshops and private consultations, Karen is able to attract your ideal clients, going beyond mere decoration by uniquely applying the physics and psychology of colour to your brand.

## MONIQUE FOK - INTERN

Having been raised in another exhilarating city, Hong Kong, for more than 20 years, Monique is a media student who's enchanted by London for its versatility and multi-cultural facet. Getting to know the inspiring women featured in this book deepened her love for this city,"I'm glad to join this celebration of women's successful work in creating a new identity for modern women."

## TOM PARKINSON - EDITOR

Tom is a digital media specialist, more often found in the midst of a creative session, working with designers and copywriters on large scale projects for international clients. His detail-oriented approach to everything from complex code to simple sentences and his years of experience making things work in print and online give him all the tools he needs to be a full-service editor. He lives in South-West London with his wife, Carlie, his son Oliver, and their chihuahua, Zorro.

## HOLLY SMITH - INTERN

Why get involved in Covet Girl? Well, why wouldn't you? What young, aspiring and dream-filled 22 year old girl could turn their nose up at a job where, day in day out, they are looking at incredible women who have achieved everything they, at some point, thought would not be possible. If you can find a more life affirming and inspirational job than that, then you must be very lucky indeed.

## MELISA THOMAS - COPY CONTRIBUTOR

Always amazed by anyone with the passion and tenacity to start their own business and make it work, Melisa found writing for Covet Girl inspiring and exciting as she heard the success stories of so many women making their own contributions to a wide range of products and services,"I'm delighted when personality and individuality triumphs over the uniformity of mass consumerism - especially when there's a woman behind the success!"

# ALPHABETICAL INDEX

## Symbols



## A



## B



## C



## D



## E



## F



## G



## H



## I



## J



## K

## Y



## Z

# CATEGORY INDEX

## ARTS AND CRAFTS



## BEAUTY



## CHILDREN



## EVENTS/ENTERTAINMENT



## FASHION



## FITNESS

## GIFTS



## HEALTH



## HOME



## INDUSTRY (B2B)



## JEWELLERY



## PETS

## PHOTOGRAPHERS



## RESTAURANTS



## SERVICES



## SPECIALTY FOOD



## TRAVEL

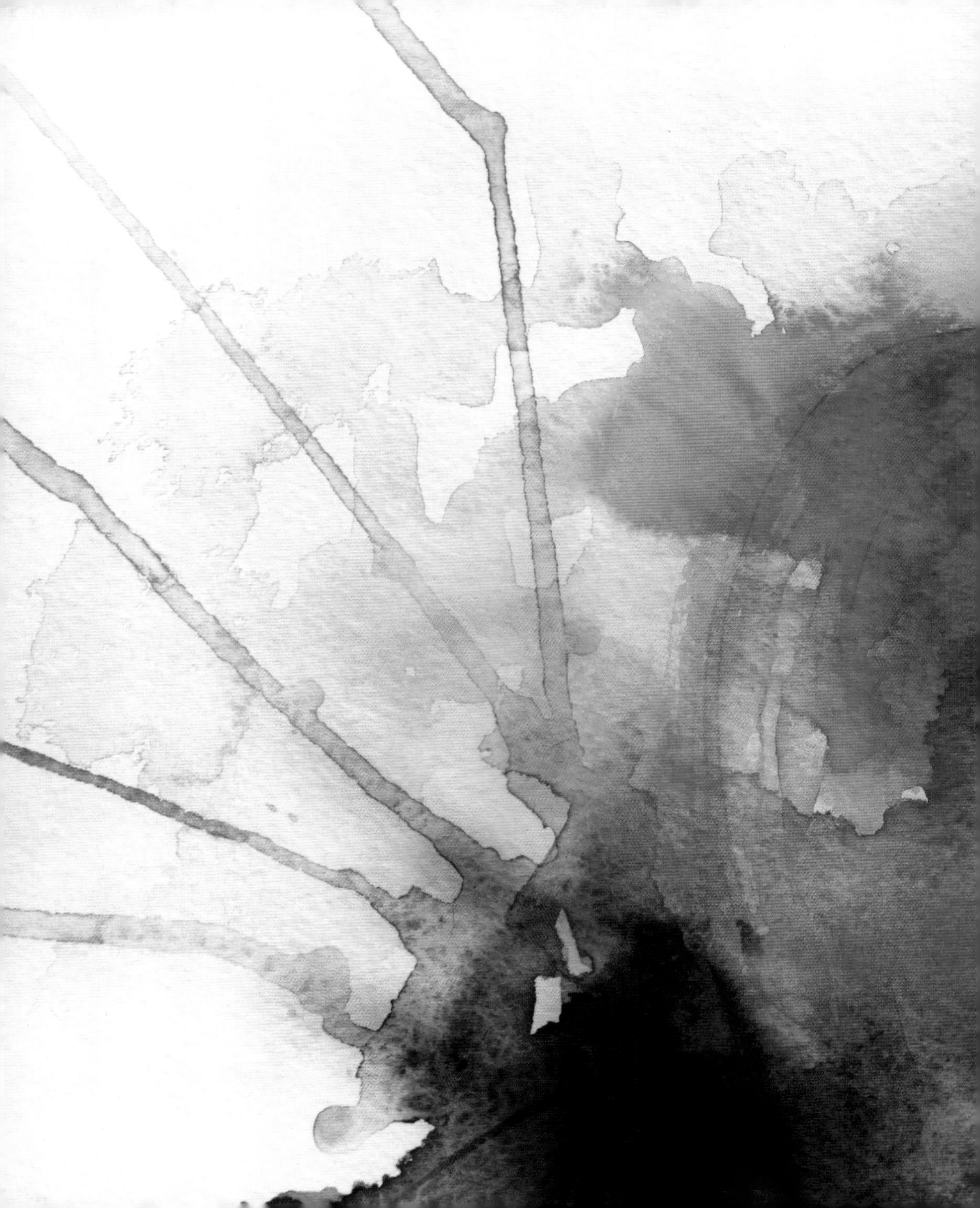

Published in 2013 by Covet Girl Publishing
www.covetgirl.com
info@covetgirl.com

Book Concept:
Carlie Smith Parkinson

Design and Art Direction:
The Pixel Pusher ltd.

Principal Photographers:
Annie Armitage, Serena Bolton, Milly Colley,
Charlotte Fielding, Beatrix Fuhrmann,
Rashmi Gill, Fanni Williams, Lucy Williams

Stock photogaphy and illustrations
from Shutterstock.com:

Front Cover - AS Photo
Back Cover - Elena Elisseeva
pg 62 - Ron Ellis
pg 30 - Pete Spiro
pg 128 - R Nagy
pg 3/4 - IR Stone
pgs 2, 238/239 - Anna Ismagilova

Project Editor:
Tom Parkinson